CW00751211

The Big Guitar Chord Songbook
Blues

Published by:
Wise Publications
14-15 Berners Street, London, W1T 3LJ, UK.

Exclusive Distributors:
Music Sales Limited Distribution Centre
Newmarket Road, Bury St Edmunds, Suffolk, IP33 3YB, UK.
Music Sales Pty Limited
120 Rothschild Avenue, Rosebery, NSW 2018, Australia.

Order No. AM984390
ISBN 978-1-84609-301-2
This book © Copyright 2007 by Wise Publications,
a division of Music Sales Limited.

Edited by Tom Farncombe.
Music arranged by Dave Weston.
Music processed by Paul Ewers Music Design.
Compiled by Nick Crispin.
Cover photograph courtesy of Deltahaze Corporation/Redferns.

Printed in the EU.

www.musicsales.com

Wise Publications
London/New York/Paris/Sydney/Copenhagen/Berlin/Madrid/Tokyo

Ain't Nobody Home

Words & Music by
Jerry Ragovoy

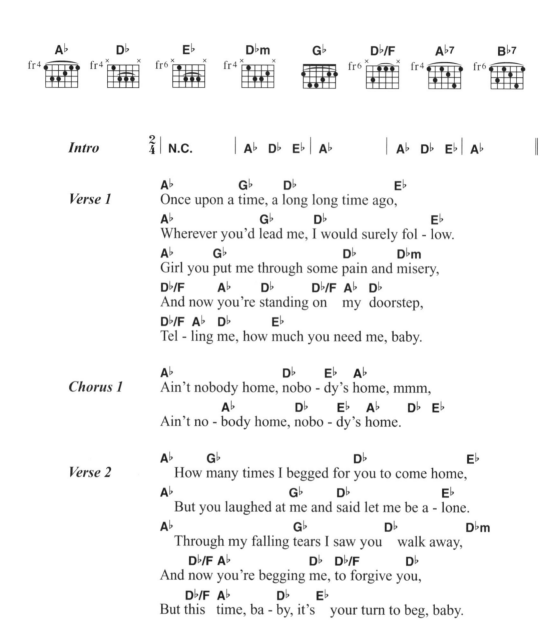

Intro $\frac{2}{4}$ | N.C. | A♭ D♭ E♭ | A♭ | A♭ D♭ E♭ | A♭ ‖

Verse 1

A♭   G♭   D♭   E♭
Once upon a time, a long long time ago,

A♭   G♭   D♭   E♭
Wherever you'd lead me, I would surely fol - low.

A♭ G♭   D♭   D♭m
Girl you put me through some pain and misery,

D♭/F A♭   D♭   D♭/F A♭ D♭
And now you're standing on   my doorstep,

D♭/F A♭ D♭   E♭
Tel - ling me, how much you need me, baby.

Chorus 1

A♭   D♭   E♭ A♭
Ain't nobody home, nobo - dy's home, mmm,

             A♭   D♭ E♭ A♭ D♭ E♭
Ain't no - body home, nobo - dy's home.

Verse 2

A♭ G♭   D♭   E♭
How many times I begged for you to come home,

A♭   G♭ D♭   E♭
But you laughed at me and said let me be a - lone.

A♭   G♭   D♭   D♭m
Through my falling tears I saw you walk away,

  D♭/F A♭   D♭ D♭/F   D♭
And now you're begging me, to forgive you,

  D♭/F A♭   D♭   E♭
But this time, ba - by, it's your turn to beg, baby.

Chorus 2

A♭   D♭ E♭ A♭
Ain't nobody home, no - body's home,

    D♭ E♭ A♭
Mmm, no - body's home,

(A♭)   D♭ E♭ A♭ D♭
Ain't nobody home, no - body's home.

Bridge

(D♭) A♭7
 Girl, I used to love you, nobody's home,

D♭   A♭7
 Placed no one else above you,

D♭   A♭7
 Gave you ev'rything that I own.

B♭7
Girl, you can't come back here,

E♭   N.C.
Ain't nobody home. Nobody's home.

Verse 3

A♭ G♭   D♭   E♭
 Once upon a time, when you went on your way,

A♭   G♭
 Girl I hoped and prayed,

 D♭   E♭
That you'd come back some - day.

A♭   G♭   D♭   D♭m
 But time has made some changes, turned me upside down.

D♭/F A♭ D♭ D♭/F D♭
 So, you can beg me to forgive you,

D♭/F A♭ D♭   E♭
 But this time, baby, you can turn right around, baby.

Repeat to fade with vocal ad lib.

Outro

‖: A♭ D♭ E♭ | A♭ | A♭ D♭ E♭ | A♭   :‖
Ain't nobody home.   Ain't nobody home.

All Your Love

Words & Music by
Otis Rush

Intro	Drums	Am7	Am7	Am7
	Am7	Dm7	Dm7	Am7
	Am7	Em7	Dm7	Am7

Verse 1

    N.C.   Am7
All the love in this loving, all the kiss in this kissing.
                Dm7   Am7
All the love in this loving, all the kiss in this kiss - ing.
                Em7 Dm7   Am7 N.C.
Before I met you baby, never knew what I was missing.

Verse 2

    (N.C.)   Am7
All your love, pretty baby, that I got in store for you.
                Dm7   Am7
All your love, pretty baby, that I got in store for you.
                Em7 Dm7   Am7 N.C.
I love you pretty baby, well I say you love me too.

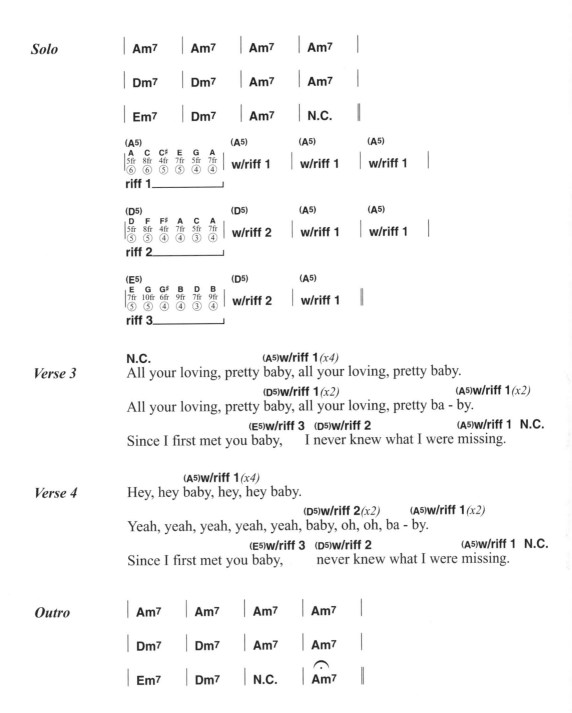

Solo

| Am⁷ | Am⁷ | Am⁷ | Am⁷ |

| Dm⁷ | Dm⁷ | Am⁷ | Am⁷ |

| Em⁷ | Dm⁷ | Am⁷ | N.C. ‖

Verse 3

N.C.　　　　　　　　　　　(A5)w/riff 1 *(x4)*
All your loving, pretty baby, all your loving, pretty baby.
　　　　　　　(D5)w/riff 1 *(x2)*　　　　　　　(A5)w/riff 1 *(x2)*
All your loving, pretty baby, all your loving, pretty ba - by.
　　　　　　　(E5)w/riff 3　(D5)w/riff 2　　　　(A5)w/riff 1　N.C.
Since I first met you baby,　　I never knew what I were missing.

Verse 4

　　　　　(A5)w/riff 1 *(x4)*
Hey, hey baby, hey, hey baby.
　　　　　　　　　　(D5)w/riff 2 *(x2)*　　(A5)w/riff 1 *(x2)*
Yeah, yeah, yeah, yeah, yeah, baby, oh, oh, ba - by.
　　　　　　　(E5)w/riff 3　(D5)w/riff 2　　　　(A5)w/riff 1　N.C.
Since I first met you baby,　　never knew what I were missing.

Outro

| Am⁷ | Am⁷ | Am⁷ | Am⁷ |

| Dm⁷ | Dm⁷ | Am⁷ | Am⁷ |

| Em⁷ | Dm⁷ | N.C. | Am⁷ ‖

7

Babe, I'm Gonna Leave You

Words & Music by Anne Bredon

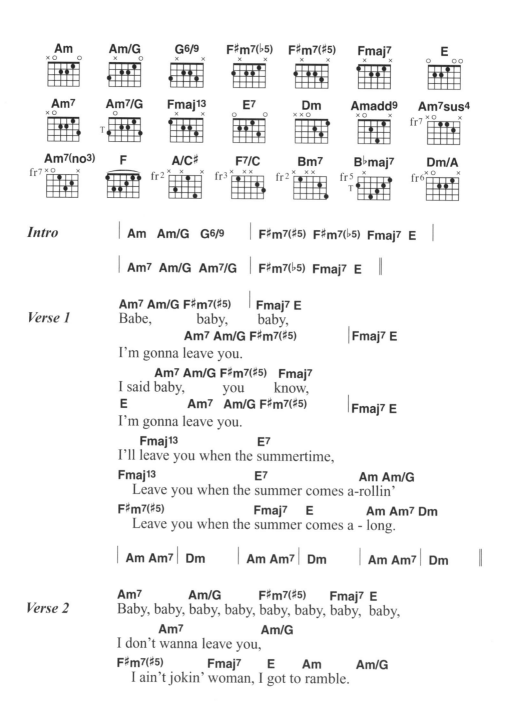

Intro

| Am Am/G G6/9 | F#m7(#5) F#m7(b5) Fmaj7 E |

| Am7 Am/G Am7/G | F#m7(b5) Fmaj7 E ||

Verse 1

Am7 Am/G F#m7(#5) | Fmaj7 E
Babe,   baby,   baby,

　　　　　Am7 Am/G F#m7(#5) | Fmaj7 E
I'm gonna leave you.

　　　　Am7 Am/G F#m7(#5)   Fmaj7
I said baby,   you   know,

　　　E   Am7   Am/G F#m7(#5) | Fmaj7 E
I'm gonna leave you.

　　Fmaj13   E7
I'll leave you when the summertime,

Fmaj13   E7   Am Am/G
　Leave you when the summer comes a-rollin'

F#m7(#5)   Fmaj7   E   Am Am7 Dm
　Leave you when the summer comes a - long.

| Am Am7 | Dm | Am Am7 | Dm | Am Am7 | Dm ||

Verse 2

Am7   Am/G   F#m7(#5)   Fmaj7 E
Baby, baby, baby, baby, baby, baby, baby, baby,

　　　　Am7   Am/G
I don't wanna leave you,

F#m7(#5)   Fmaj7   E   Am   Am/G
　I ain't jokin' woman, I got to ramble.

cont.

F#m7(#5) Fmaj7 E Am7 Am/G   F#m7(#5)
Oh,   yeah,   baby, baby, I be - lievin',

  Fmaj7 E   Fmaj13 E7
We really got to ramble.

Fmaj13   E7   Am7   Am/G
  I can hear it callin' me the way it used to do,

F#m7(#5)   Fmaj7 E   Am Dm
  I can hear it callin' me back home!

| Am Am7| Dm | Am Am7| Dm | Am Am7| Dm |

Instrumental. ‖: Amadd9   Am7(no3) | Am7sus4   Dm/A   :‖ *Play 4 times*

Chorus 1

Am Am/G F#m7(#5) F   E   Am   Am/G F#m7(#5) F E
Babe——   I'm gonna leave you.

   Am Am/G F#m7(#5)   F
Oh, ba - by,   you know,

   E   Am   Am/G F#m7(#5)
I've really got to leave you.

F   E F   E
  Oh,   I can hear it callin' me,

F   E   Am Am7 Dm
  I said don't you hear it callin' me the way it used to do?

| Am Am7| Dm | Am Am7| Dm | Am Am7| Dm   ‖

Guitar solo | Am   Am/G | F#m7(#5) Fmaj7 E | Am   Am/G | F#m7(#5) Fmaj7 E ‖

Verse 3

Am   Am/G   F#m7(#5)   Fmaj7
  I know, I know, I know, I never, never, never,

  E   Am   Am/G
Never, gonna leave your babe.

F#m7(#5)   Fmaj7   E
  But I got to go away from this place,

Am7 Am/G   F#m7(#5) Fmaj7 E
  I've got to quit you, yeah,

Am   Am/G F#m7(#5) Fmaj7 E
Baby, baby, baby,   baby.

Chorus 2

Am   Am/G F#m7(#5) F E
Baby, baby, baby,   ohh.

Am   Am/G F#m7(#5)   F   E
  Don't you hear it callin' me?

Verse 4

Am Am/G G6/9 Fmaj7(♭5) F♯m7(♯5) Fmaj7 E
        Wo - man,

Am   Am/G Fmaj7(♭5) Fmaj7 E
Woman,   I know,   I know,

           Am   Am/G
It feels good to have you back a - gain

                        F♯m7(♯5)   Fmaj7 E   Am   Am/G
And I know that one day baby, it's really gonna grow, yes it is.

           Fmaj7(♭5)   Fmaj7 E   Am
We gonna go walkin' through the park every day.

Chorus 3

Am/G   F♯m7(♯5)   F E
   Come what may, every day,

Am Am/G F♯m7(♯5)   F   E
                                    I got to leave you

Am Am/G F♯m7(♯5)   Fmaj7   E
Woman.

Verse 5

Am Am/G F♯m7(♭5) Fmaj7 E

Am Am/G F♯m7(♭5) Fmaj7 E

Am Am/G F♯m7(♭5) Fmaj7 E
 It was really, really

Am   Am/G F♯m7(♯5)   Fmaj7   E   Am
good.   You made me happy every single day

Am/G   F♯m7(♯5)   Fmaj7 E   Am
      But now——   I've got to go away!

Chorus 4

Am/G F♯m7(♯5) F   E

Am   Am/G F♯m7(♯5) F   E

Am   Am/G F♯m7(♯5) F   E

Am   Am/G F♯m7(♯5) F   E
   Baby, baby,   baby,

Outro

F   E7
That's when it's callin' me,

F   E   A/C♯ F7/C B♭m7 B♭maj7 Amadd9
   I said that's when it's callin' me back home.

Ball And Biscuit

Words & Music by
Jack White

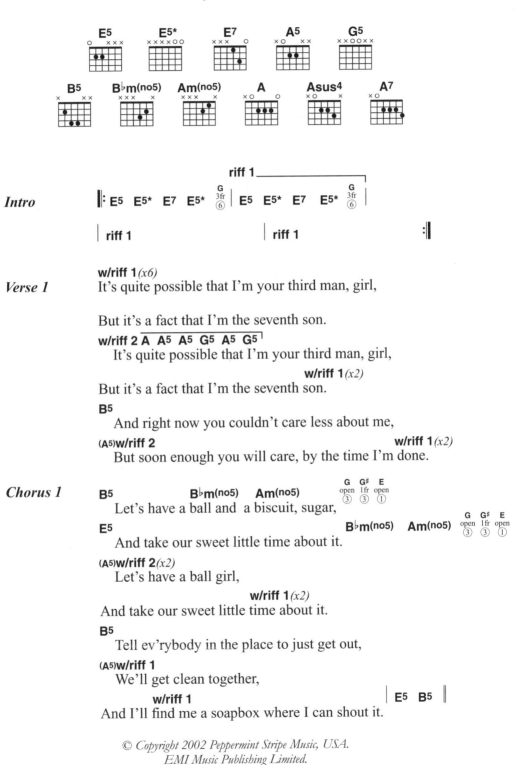

Intro

‖: E5 E5* E7 E5* G 3fr 6 | E5 E5* E7 E5* G 3fr 6 |

| riff 1 | riff 1 | :‖

Verse 1

w/riff 1 *(x6)*
It's quite possible that I'm your third man, girl,

But it's a fact that I'm the seventh son.

w/riff 2 A A5 A5 G5 A5 G5
It's quite possible that I'm your third man, girl,

w/riff 1 *(x2)*
But it's a fact that I'm the seventh son.

B5
And right now you couldn't care less about me,

(A5)w/riff 2   w/riff 1 *(x2)*
But soon enough you will care, by the time I'm done.

Chorus 1

B5   B♭m(no5)   Am(no5)   G G♯ E open 1fr open ③ ③ ①
Let's have a ball and a biscuit, sugar,

E5   B♭m(no5)   Am(no5)   G G♯ E open 1fr open ③ ③ ①
And take our sweet little time about it.

(A5)w/riff 2 *(x2)*
Let's have a ball girl,

                        w/riff 1 *(x2)*
And take our sweet little time about it.

B5
Tell ev'rybody in the place to just get out,

(A5)w/riff 1
We'll get clean together,

        w/riff 1 | E5 B5 ‖
And I'll find me a soapbox where I can shout it.

Instr. 1		E5		E5		E5		E5		

Instr. 1

E5	E5	E5	E5	
A5	A5	E5	E5	
B5	A5	E5 /G♯ /A /A♯	B5	‖

Link 1

riff 1	riff 1	riff 1	riff 1	‖

Verse 2

w/riff 1 *(x4)*
You read it in the newspaper,

                                                 A Asus4 A
Ask your girlfriends and see if they know.

(A)   **A Asus4 A**
  You read it in the newspaper,

(A)   **w/riff 1** *(x2)*
  Ask your girlfriends and see if they know.

B5
  That my strength is ten-fold girl,

(A5)w/riff 2   **w/riff 1** *(x2)*
  I'll let you see it if you want to before you go.

Chorus 2

		G	G♯	E
		open	1fr	open
		③	③	①

B5   **B♭m(no5) Am(no5)**
  Let's have a ball and a biscuit, sugar,

E5   **B♭m(no5) Am(no5)**
  And take our sweet little time about it.

(A5)w/riff 2 *(x2)*
  Let's have a ball,

                       w/riff 1 *(x2)*
And take our sweet little time about it.

B5
  Tell ev'rybody in the place to just get out,

(A5)w/riff 1
  We'll get clean together,

         w/riff 1
And I'll find me a soapbox where I can shout it.

E5   **B5**
And I can think of one or two things to say about it... alright, listen.

| *Instr. 2* | As Instr. 1 |

Link 2		riff 1		riff 1		riff 1		riff 1		
		Asus⁴ A A⁷		Asus⁴ A A⁷		riff 1		riff 1		
		B⁵		A⁷		riff 1		E⁵ B⁵	‖

Instr. 3	‖: E⁵		E⁵		E⁵		E⁵		
	A⁵		A⁵		E⁵		E⁵		
	B⁵		A⁵		E⁵ /G♯ /A /A♯		B⁵	:‖

| *Link 3* | As Link 1 |

w/riff 1 *(x4)*

Verse 3   It's quite possible that I'm your third man,

But it's a fact that I'm the seventh son.

(A⁵)w/riff 2 *(x2)*
    It was the other two which made me your third,

                                    w/riff 1 *(x2)*
But it's my mother who made me the se - venth son.

B⁵
    And right now you couldn't care less about me,

(A⁵)w/riff 2   **E⁵**
    But soon enough you will care by the time I'm done.

Yeah, you just wait. You stick around. You figure it out.

Baby, Please Don't Go

Words & Music by
Joe Williams

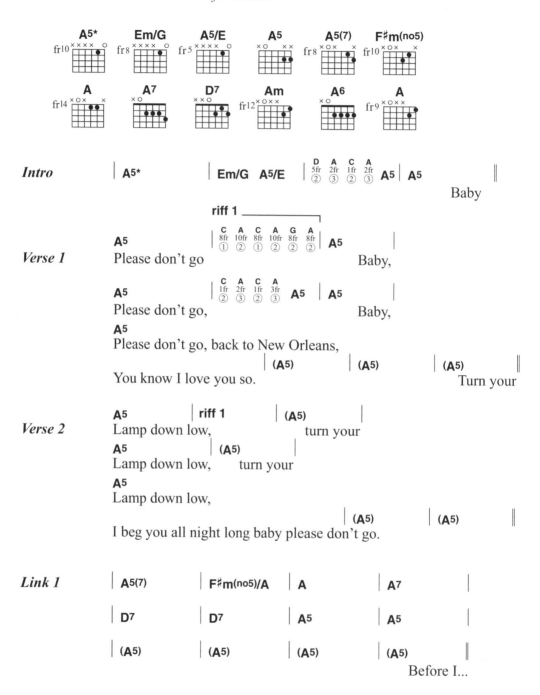

Intro | A5* | | Em/G   A5/E | A5 | A5 ‖

Baby

Verse 1   A5   A5 |

Please don't go   Baby,

A5   A5 | A5 |

Please don't go,   Baby,

A5

Please don't go, back to New Orleans,

| (A5) | (A5) | (A5) ‖

You know I love you so.   Turn your

Verse 2   A5 | **riff 1** | (A5) |

Lamp down low,   turn your

A5 | (A5) |

Lamp down low,   turn your

A5

Lamp down low,

| (A5) | (A5) ‖

I beg you all night long baby please don't go.

Link 1 | A5(7) | F♯m(no5)/A | A | A7 |

| D7 | D7 | A5 | A5 |

| (A5) | (A5) | (A5) | (A5) ‖

Before I...

Verse 3

A5 | riff 1 | (A5) |
Be your dog, before I

A5 | (A5) |
Be your dog, before I

A5
Be your dog,

I get you way down here

| (A5) | (A5) ‖
And I'd make you walk the log ba - by.

Link 2

| A5 | A5 | Am | A |

| Am | A | D7 | D7 |

| A5 | A5 | A5 | A5 |

| A5 ‖
Well your...

Verse 4

A5 | riff 1 | (A5) |
Man has gone, well your

A5 | (A5) |
Man has gone, well your

A5
Man has gone,

To the county farm,

| (A5) | (A5) ‖
He got the shackles on, baby.

Outro

| (A5) | A6 A7 ‖

Baby, What You Want Me To Do?

Words & Music by
Jimmy Reed

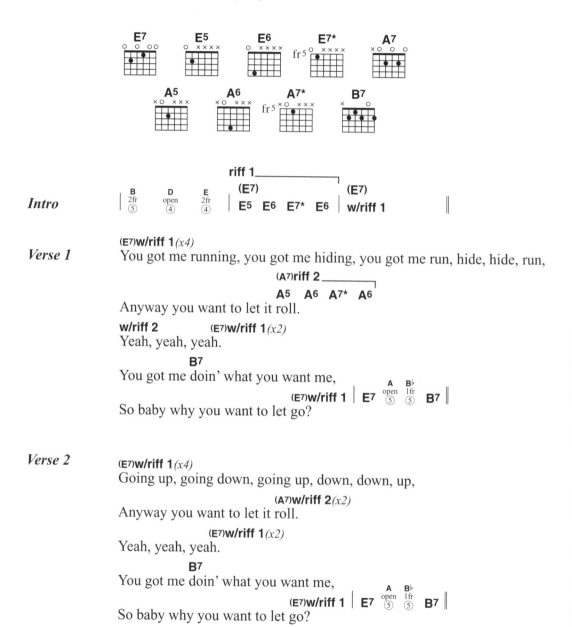

Intro

riff 1
(E7) | E5 E6 E7* E6 | (E7) w/riff 1 ‖

Verse 1

(E7)**w/riff 1** *(x4)*
You got me running, you got me hiding, you got me run, hide, hide, run,

(A7)**riff 2**
A5 A6 A7* A6
Anyway you want to let it roll.

w/riff 2   (E7)**w/riff 1** *(x2)*
Yeah, yeah, yeah.

B7
You got me doin' what you want me,

(E7)**w/riff 1** | E7 A B♭ B7 ‖
So baby why you want to let go?

Verse 2

(E7)**w/riff 1** *(x4)*
Going up, going down, going up, down, down, up,

(A7)**w/riff 2** *(x2)*
Anyway you want to let it roll.

(E7)**w/riff 1** *(x2)*
Yeah, yeah, yeah.

B7
You got me doin' what you want me,

(E7)**w/riff 1** | E7 A B♭ B7 ‖
So baby why you want to let go?

Instr.

(E7)w/riff 1 *(x4)*	E7		E7		E7	

(A7)w/riff 2 *(x2)*	A7		(E7)w/riff 1 *(x2)*	E7	

B7		B7		(E7)w/riff 1	E7 A open ⑤ B♭ 1fr ⑤ B7

Verse 3

(E7)w/riff 1 *(x4)*
You got me beeping, you got me hiding, you got me beep, hide, hide, beep,

(A7)w/riff 2 *(x2)*
Anyway you want to let it roll.

(E7)w/riff 1 *(x2)*
Yeah, yeah, yeah.

B7
You got me doin' what you want me,

(E7)w/riff 1 | E7 A open ⑤ B♭ 1fr ⑤ B7 ‖
So baby why you want to let go?

Outro

As Instr. *To fade.*

Bad To The Bone

Words & Music by
George Thorogood

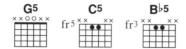

⑥ = **D**   ③ = **G**
⑤ = **G**   ② = **B**
④ = **D**   ① = **D**

Intro   ‖: *G5 G5 C5 G5 B♭5 G5 | G5 G5 C5 G5 B♭5 G5 :‖

riff

‖: G5   G5 G5 C5 G5 B♭5 G5 | w/riff   :‖

w/riff throughout

Verse 1   On the day I was born,

The nurses all I gathered 'round

And they gazed in wide wonder,

At the joy they had found.

The head nurse spoke up,

Said "leave this one alone"

She could tell right away

That I was bad to the bone.

w/riff

Chorus 1   Bad to the bone.

Bad to the bone.

B-B-B-B-Bad to the bone.

B-B-B-B-Bad

B-B-B-B-Bad

Bad to the bone.

w/riff throughout

Verse 2   I broke a thousand hearts,

Before I met you.

I'll break a thousand more, baby

Before I am through.

I wanna be yours pretty baby,

Yours and yours alone.

I'm here to tell ya honey,

That I'm bad to the bone.

w/riff

Chorus 2   Bad to the bone.

B-B-B-Bad

B-B-B-Bad

B-B-B-Bad

Bad to the bone.

Solo 1   ‖: w/riff | w/riff | w/riff | w/riff :‖ *Play 3 times*

| G5 ‖

Verse 3

N.C
I make a rich woman beg,
w/riff
I'll make a good woman steal.

I'll make an old woman blush,

And make a young girl squeal.

I wanna be yours pretty baby,

Yours and yours alone.

I'm here to tell ya honey,

That I'm bad to the bone.

Chorus 3

w/riff
B-B-B-B-Bad

B-B-B-B-Bad

B-B-B-B-Bad

Bad to the bone.

Solo 2 ‖: **w/riff** | **w/riff** | **w/riff** | **w/riff** :‖ *Play 8 times*

Verse 4

w/riff throughout

And when I walk the streets,

Kings and Queens step aside.

Every woman I meet,

They all stay satisfied.

I wanna tell ya pretty baby,

Well ya see I make my own.

I'm here to tell ya honey,

That I'm bad to the bone.

Chorus 4

w/riff

Bad to the bone.

B-B-B-B-Bad

B-B-B-Bad

B-B-B-Bad

Whoo, bad to the bone.

Outro ‖: w/riff | w/riff | w/riff | w/riff :‖ G⁵ ‖

Play 3 times

Bell Bottom Blues

Words & Music by
Eric Clapton

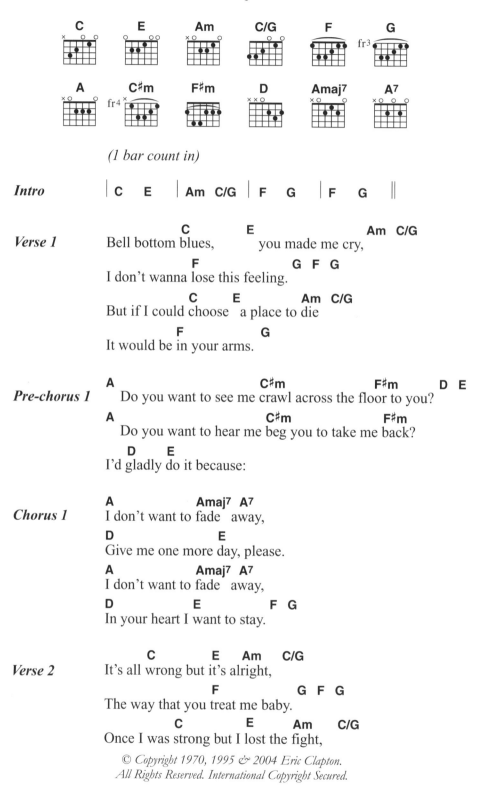

(1 bar count in)

Intro | C E | Am C/G | F G | F G ||

Verse 1

              C   E   Am C/G

Bell bottom blues,   you made me cry,

              F   G F G

I don't wanna lose this feeling.

                 C   E   Am C/G

But if I could choose   a place to die

             F   G

It would be in your arms.

Pre-chorus 1

   A   C#m   F#m   D E

Do you want to see me crawl across the floor to you?

   A   C#m   F#m

Do you want to hear me beg you to take me back?

   D   E

I'd gladly do it because:

Chorus 1

   A   Amaj7 A7

I don't want to fade   away,

   D   E

Give me one more day, please.

   A   Amaj7 A7

I don't want to fade   away,

   D   E   F G

In your heart I want to stay.

Verse 2

           C   E   Am   C/G

It's all wrong but it's alright,

                   F   G F G

The way that you treat me baby.

            C   E   Am C/G

Once I was strong but I lost the fight,

                F   **G**

cont.   You won't find a better loser.

Pre-chorus 2   As Pre-chorus 1

Chorus 2   As Chorus 1

Instrumental | C   E | Am C/G | F   G | F   G |

              | C   E | Am C/G | F   G ||

Pre-chorus 3   As Pre-chorus 1

Chorus 3   As Chorus 1

                      C   **E**   **Am**   **C/G**

Verse 3   Bell bottom blues,   don't say goodbye,

                               F   **G** **F** **G**

              We're surely gonna meet again.

                     C   **E**   **Am**   **C/G**

              And if we do don't you be surprised

                          F   **G**

              If you find me with another lover.

Pre-chorus 4   As Pre-chorus 1

                 A   **Amaj⁷ A⁷**

Chorus 4   ‖: I don't want to fade   away,

                 D   **E**

              Give me one more day, please.

                 A   **Amaj⁷ A⁷**

              I don't want to fade   away,

                 D   **E**

              In your heart I want to stay. :‖

                 A   **Amaj⁷ A⁷**

              I don't want to fade   away,

                 D   **E**

              Give me one more day, please.

                 A   **Amaj⁷ A⁷**

              I don't want to fade   away,

                 D   **E**   **F G**

              In your heart I want to stay.

Black Betty

Words & Music by
Huddie Ledbetter

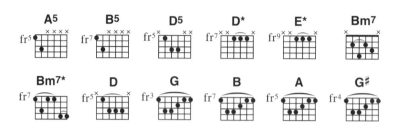

A5	B5	D5	D*	E*	Bm7

Bm7*	D	G	B	A	G#

Intro |N.C. |N.C. A5 |B5 N.C. A5 |B5 D |D   A5 ‖: B5 D* E D* A5 :‖ *x4*

|B5   E |B5   D|B5   E|B5   D|B5 |B5 |B |B |

Verse 1

Bm7   N.C.
Whoa, Black Betty (bam-ba-lam)

Whoa, Black Betty (bam-ba-lam)
                  Bm7   N.C.
Black Betty had a child   (bam-ba-lam)
                 Bm7*   N.C.
The damn thing gone wild   (bam-ba-lam)
                          Bm7   N.C.
She said 'I'm worryin' outta mind'   (bam-ba-lam)
                   Bm7*   N.C.
The damn thing gone blind   (bam-ba-lam)
                Bm7   N.C.
I said Oh, Black Betty   (bam-ba-lam)
               Bm*   N.C.   A5
Whoa, Black Betty   (bam-ba-lam)

Instrumental |B5 N.C. A5 |B5 D |D   A5 ‖: B5 D* E D* A5 :‖ *x4*

|B5   E |B5   D|B5   E|B5 D |B5 |

Verse 2

Bm7 N.C.
Oh, Black Betty (bam-ba-lam)

Whoa, Black Betty (bam-ba-lam)

                          Bm7   N.C.
She really gets me high   (bam-ba-lam)

                      Bm7*   N.C.
You know that's no lie   (bam-ba-lam)

                   Bm7   N.C.
She's so rock steady   (bam-ba-lam)

                   Bm7*   N.C.
And she's always ready   (bam-ba-lam)

                Bm7   N.C.
Whoa, Black Betty   (bam-ba-lam)

                Bm7*   N.C.
Whoa, Black Betty   (bam-ba-lam)

Double time:

Instrumental

| D E D |(D) | B5 D ‖: D E D |(D) |

                      |1. |2.

| B5 | N.C. | N.C. | N.C. | N.C. D :‖ N.C. D |
(drum solo) _____

| D E D |(D) | B5 | B5 | B5 | B5 | B5 | N.C. | N.C. |

‖: D | D | D | D | G | G | D | D |

| B | B | B | B   :‖

                                       x3

‖: D | D | D | D | B | B | B | B   :‖

Normal time |1. |2.

‖: B A | B A D | B A | A D :‖ A G# |

Double time:

|(B)N.C. | N.C. | N.C. | N.C. D |
(drum solo) _____

| D E D |(D) | B5 | N.C. | N.C. | N.C. | N.C. D | D E D |(D) |
              (drum solo) _____

| B5 | B5 | B5 | B5 | B5 | B | B | B | B |

Verse 3

N.C.
Whoa, Black Betty (bam-ba-lam)

Whoa, Black Betty (bam-ba-lam)

Bm⁷   **N.C.**
She's from Birmingham   (bam-ba-lam)

Bm⁷*   **N.C.**
Way down in Alabam'   (bam-ba-lam)

Bm⁷   **N.C.**
Well, she's shakin' that thing   (bam-ba-lam)

Bm⁷*   **N.C.**
Boy, she makes me sing   (bam-ba-lam)

Bm⁷   **N.C.**
Whoa, Black Betty   (bam-ba-lam)

Bm⁷*   **Bm⁷**
Whoa, Black Betty   (BAM-BA-LAM)

Death Letter Blues

Words & Music by
Son House

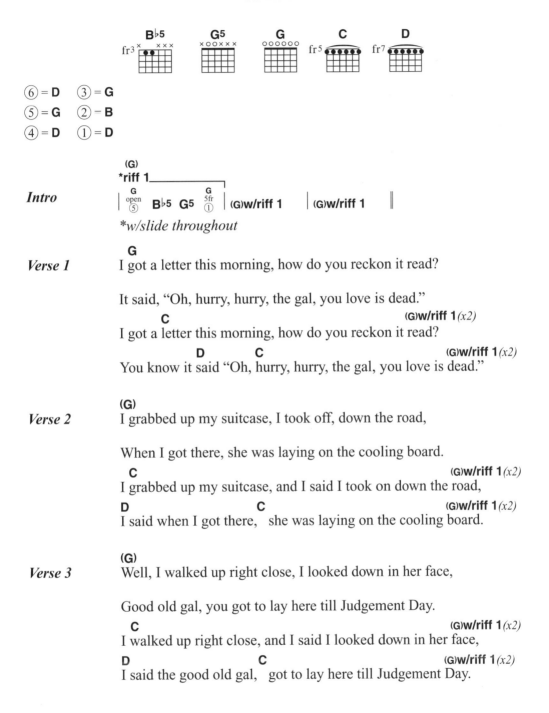

⑥ = D   ③ = G
⑤ = G   ② = B
④ = D   ① = D

(G)
***riff 1**_____

Intro | G open ⑤   B♭5 G5 G 5fr ① | **(G)w/riff 1** | **(G)w/riff 1** ‖

*w/slide throughout

Verse 1

G
I got a letter this morning, how do you reckon it read?

It said, "Oh, hurry, hurry, the gal, you love is dead."
        C   **(G)w/riff 1** *(x2)*
I got a letter this morning, how do you reckon it read?
         D   **C**   **(G)w/riff 1** *(x2)*
You know it said "Oh, hurry, hurry, the gal, you love is dead."

Verse 2

(G)
I grabbed up my suitcase, I took off, down the road,

When I got there, she was laying on the cooling board.
     C   **(G)w/riff 1** *(x2)*
I grabbed up my suitcase, and I said I took on down the road,
D   **C**   **(G)w/riff 1** *(x2)*
I said when I got there,   she was laying on the cooling board.

Verse 3

(G)
Well, I walked up right close, I looked down in her face,

Good old gal, you got to lay here till Judgement Day.
     C   **(G)w/riff 1** *(x2)*
I walked up right close, and I said I looked down in her face,
D   **C**   **(G)w/riff 1** *(x2)*
I said the good old gal,   got to lay here till Judgement Day.

Verse 4

(G)
Looked like there was ten thousand people standing

Round the buryin' ground,

I didn't know I loved her till they let her down.

C   (G)w/riff 1 *(x2)*
Looked like ten thousand people standing round the buryin' ground,
D   C   (G)w/riff 1 *(x2)*
You know I didn't know I loved her   till they damn let her down.

Verse 5

(G)
Well I folded up my arms, and I slowly walked away,

I said "farewell honey, I'll see you Judgement Day."
C   (G)w/riff 1 *(x2)*
Yes, oh yes I walked a - way,
        D   C   (G)w/riff 1 *(x2)*
I said "farewell, farewell, and I'll see you Judgement Day."

Verse 6

(G)
You know I didn't feel so bad, till the good old sun went down,

I didn't have a soul to throw my arms around.
C   (G)w/riff 1 *(x2)*
I didn't feel so bad, till the good old sun went down,
D   C   (G)w/riff 1 *(x2)*
Mmm.   Mmm.

Verse 7

(G)
You know it's so hard to love someone that don't love you,

Ain't no satisfaction, don't care what you do.
C   (G)w/riff 1 *(x2)*
Yeah it's so hard to love someone who don't love you,
        D   C   (G)w/riff 1 *(x2)*
You know it look like it ain't satisfaction,   don't care what you do.

Verse 8

(G)
Well I got this morning, at the break of day,

Just a-huggin' the pillow where she used to lay.

C   (G)w/riff 1 *(x2)*
I said "I got up this morning, yes at break of day,

D
You know I was a-huggin' the pillow,

          C   (G)w/riff 1 *(x2)*
Where my good gal used to lay."

Verse 9

(G)
I got up this morning, feeling around for my shoes,

You know I must-a had them walkin' blues.

C   (G)w/riff 1 *(x2)*
Got up this morning, feeling around for my shoes,

D   C   (G)w/riff 1 *(x2)*
Yeah you know about that,   I must-a had them walkin' blues.

Verse 10

(G)
Ah hush, I thought I heard her call my name,

If it wasn't so loud and so nice and plain.

C   (G)w/riff 1 *(x2)*
Yes mmm. Mmm.

D   C | (G)w/riff 1 | (G)w/riff 1 | G ||
Mmm.   Mmm.

Black Magic Woman

Words & Music by
Peter Green

Dm*   Dm   Am   Gm   C   A7   B♭

Intro   Dm*

Verse 1
                                  Dm
I've got a Black Magic Woman
                                Am
I've got a Black Magic Woman
            Dm
Yes I've got a Black Magic Woman,
                   Gm
Got me so blind I can't see
          Dm   **C**
That she's a Black Magic Woman
        B♭   **A7**   **Dm**   **Dm***
And she's tryin' to make a devil out of me.

Verse 2
                              Dm
Don't turn your back on me baby,
                              Am
Don't turn your back on me baby,
                    Dm
Yes don't turn your back on me baby,
                            Gm
You're messing around with your tricks,
          Dm   **C**
Don't turn your back on me baby,
        B♭   **A7**   **Dm**   **Dm***
'Cause you might just break up my magic stick.

Guitar solo

‖: Dm | Dm | Am | Am |

| Dm | Dm | Gm | Gm |

| Dm C | B♭ A7 Dm | Dm :‖   Dm*

Verse 3

          Dm
You got your spell on me baby,

             Am
You got your spell on me babe,

        Dm
Yes you got your spell on me baby,

          Gm
Turning my heart into stone,

Dm   **C**   **B♭**   **A⁷**   **Dm**
I need you so bad, magic woman I can't leave you a - lone.

Outro

      Dm
‖: Yes, I need you so bad,

I need you darlin',

I need you darlin',

Yes I want you to love me,

I want you to love me,

I want you to love me,

Oh yeah,

Oh, baby.

Yes I need your love,

Oh I need your love so bad,

Yes I want you to love me... :‖

Repeat to fade

✳ **Boom Boom**

Words & Music by
John Lee Hooker

F   B♭   fr3   C   F7   B♭7   fr3   C7

Intro

| N.C. (riff) | F | | N.C. (riff) | F | |

| N.C. (riff) | B♭ | | N.C. (riff) | F | |

| N.C. (riff) | C | | N.C. (riff) | F | ‖

Verse 1

N.C. | F |
Boom boom boom boom,

N.C. | F |
I'm gonna shoot you right down,

N.C. | B♭ |
Right off-a your feet.

N.C. | F |
Take you home with me,

N.C. | C |
Put you in my house,

N.C. | F |
Boom boom boom boom.

Verse 2

N.C. | F |
A-haw haw haw haw,

N.C. | F |
Hmmm hmmm hmmm hmmm,

N.C. | B♭ |
Hmmm hmmm hmmm hmmm.

N.C. | F |
I love to see you strut,

N.C. | C |
Up and down the floor.

N.C. | F |
When you talking to me,

N.C. | F |
That baby talk.

cont.

N.C.   **F5**

I like it like that,

N.C.

Whoa, yeah!

Instr.

F7	**F7**	**F7**	**F7**
	(1° only) Talk that talk.	*(1° only)* Walk that walk.	
B♭7	**B♭7**	**F7**	**F7**
C7	**C7**	**F7**	**F7**

Play 3 times

Verse 3

N.C.   **F5**

But you walk that walk,

N.C.   **F5**

And talk that talk,

N.C.   **B♭5**

And whisper in my ear,

N.C.   **F5**

Tell me that you love me,

N.C.   **C5**

I love that talk.

N.C.   **F5**

When you talk like that,

N.C.   **F5**

You knocks me out,

N.C.   **F5**

Right off of my feet,

N.C.   **F5**

Ho ho ho.

Outro

F7

‖: Talk that talk, and walk that walk… :‖ *Repeat to fade*

Born Under A Bad Sign

Words & Music by
William Bell & Booker T. Jones

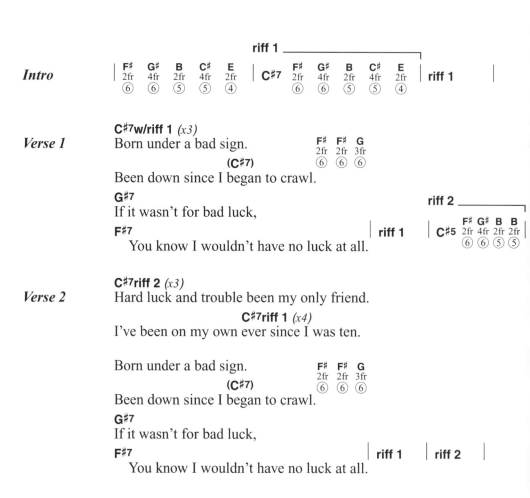

Verse 3

C♯7 w/riff 2 *(x3)*
I can't read, I didn't learn how to write.

           riff 1 *(x4)*
My whole life has been one big fight.

Born under a bad sign.
    (C♯7)
I've been down since I began to crawl.

G♯7
If it wasn't for bad luck,

F♯7 | **riff 1** | **riff 2** |
  I said I wouldn't have no luck at all.   That ain't no lie.

Solo | **riff 2** | **riff 2** | **riff 2** | **riff 2** ‖

G♯7   **(G♯7) A7 G♯7 G7**
  You know if it wasn't for bad luck,

F♯7   **G7**
I wouldn't have no kind-a luck.

G♯7   **(G♯7) A7 G♯7 G7**
  If it wasn't for real bad luck,

F♯7 N.C. | **riff 1** | **riff 2** |
I wouldn't have no luck at all.

Verse 4

riff 2 *(x3)*
You know, wine and women is all I crave.

          riff 1 *(x4)*
A big legged woman gonna carry me to my grave.

Born under a bad sign.
    (C♯7)
I've been down since I began to crawl.

G♯7
If it wasn't for bad luck,

F♯7 | **riff 1** | **riff 2** |
  I tell ya, I wouldn't have no luck at all.

Outro

w/riff 2
‖: Yeah, my bad luck boy

Been havin' bad luck all of my days, yes. :‖ *Repeat to fade*

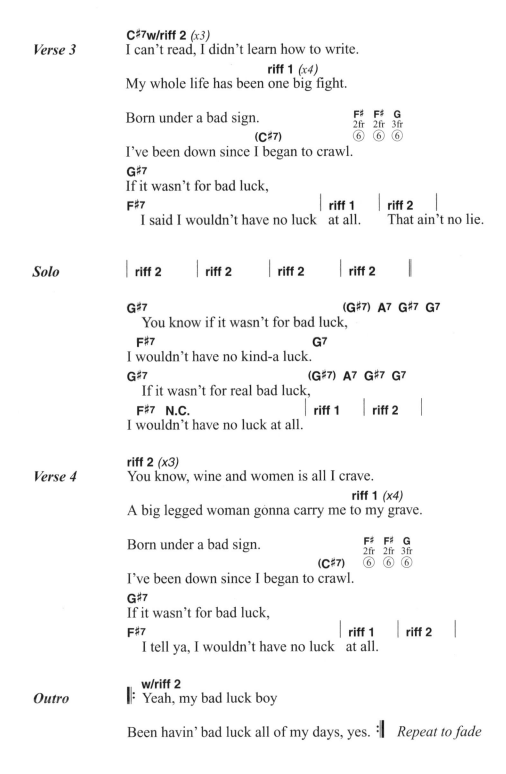

F♯ 2fr ⑥ F♯ 2fr ⑥ G 3fr ⑥

Bright Lights, Big City

Words & Music by
Jimmy Reed

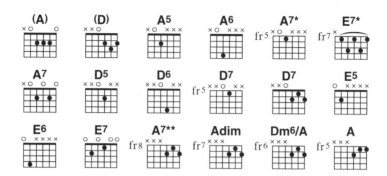

Intro

| (A)   (D) | A5 A6 A7* A6 | A5 A6 A7* A6 | A5 | D D# 5fr 6fr ⑤ ⑤ E7* |

riff 1

Verse 1

(A7)**w/riff 1** *(x4)*
Bright lights, big city, gone to my baby's head.

(D7)**w/riff 2** D6 D5 D6 D7 D6
Bright   lights, big city,

(A7)**w/riff 1** *(x2)*
  Gone to my baby's head.

(E7) E5   E6 E5   E6   (D7)**w/riff 2**   (A5)
I   tried to tell the woman but she don't believe a word I say.

riff 3

| A5 A7** Adim Dm6/A A | D D# 5fr 6fr ⑤ ⑤ E7* |
(say.)

Verse 2

(A7)**w/riff 1** *(x4)*
Go light pretty baby, gonna need my help some day.

(D7)**w/riff 2** *(x2)*   (A7)**w/riff 1** *(x2)*
It's alright pretty baby, gonna need my help some day.

E7   (E5)   (E6)   (E5)
You're gonna wish you had listen - ed,

    (D7)**w/riff 2** | (A5)**w/riff 3** | (E7*)**w/riff 3** ‖
To some of things I   said.

Instr.	(A7)w/riff 1 *(x4)*	A7	A7	A7	
	(D7)w/riff 2 *(x2)*	D7	(A7)w/riff 1 *(x2)*	A7	
	E7 (E6) (E5) (E6)	(D7)w/riff 2	(A7)w/riff 3	A7 E7*	

Verse 3

(A7)w/riff 1 *(x4)*
Go ahead pretty baby, oh honey, knock yourself out.
   (D7)w/riff 2 *(x2)*   (A7)w/riff 1 *(x2)*
Go ahead pretty baby, oh honey, knock yourself out.
    E5   E6 E5
I still love you baby
                       (A5)   (E7*)
E6   (D7)w/riff 2 | riff 3 | (riff 3)
'Cause you don't know what it's all   about.

Verse 4

(A7)w/riff 1 *(x4)*
Bright lights, big city, they went to my baby's head.
   (D7)w/riff 2 *(x2)*   (A7)w/riff 1 *(x2)*
Bright lights, big city, they went to my baby's head. *To fade*

Call It Stormy Monday (But Tuesday Is Just As Bad)

Words & Music by
T-Bone Walker

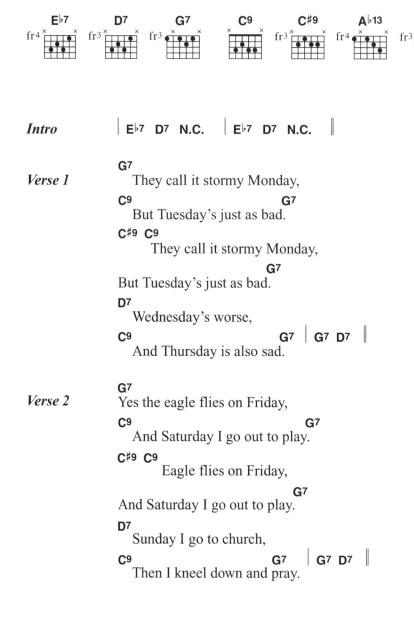

Intro | E♭7 D7 N.C. | E♭7 D7 N.C. ‖

Verse 1

G7
They call it stormy Monday,

C9   G7
But Tuesday's just as bad.

C♯9 C9
They call it stormy Monday,

                                          G7
But Tuesday's just as bad.

D7
Wednesday's worse,

C9   G7 | G7 D7 ‖
And Thursday is also sad.

Verse 2

G7
Yes the eagle flies on Friday,

C9   G7
And Saturday I go out to play.

C♯9 C9
Eagle flies on Friday,

                                          G7
And Saturday I go out to play.

D7
Sunday I go to church,

C9   G7 | G7 D7 ‖
Then I kneel down and pray.

Instr.

G7	C9	G7	G7	
C9	C9	G7	G7	
D7	C9	G7	G7 D7 ‖

Verse 3

G7
   Lord have mercy,
C9   G7
   Lord have mercy on me.
C#9 C9
     Lord have mercy,
                   G7
My heart's in misery.
D7
   Crazy about my baby,
C9   G7 | A♭13 G13 ‖
   Yes, send her back to me.

Change E.

*Cocaine

Words & Music by
J. J. Cale

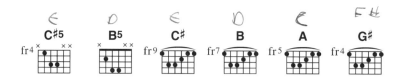

E   D   E   D   C   F#

C#5   B5   C#   B   A   G#

riff 1

Intro   C#5 C#5 B5 C#5   B5   (B5)   *Play 4 times*

Verse 1   w/riff 1 *(x4)*
If you want to hang out, you've got to take her out, cocaine.

If you want to get down, get down on the ground, cocaine.
                 C#   B   A G# N.C.
She don't lie, she don't lie, she don't lie,   cocaine.

Link 1   C#5 C#5 B5 C#5   B5   (B5)

Verse 2   w/riff 1 *(x4)*
If you got bad news, you want to kick them blues, cocaine.

When your day is done, and you want to run, cocaine.
                 C#   B   A G# N.C.
She don't lie, she don't lie, she don't lie,   cocaine.

Link 2   C#5 C#5 B5 C#5   B5   (B5)

Instr.   C#5 C#5 B5 C#5   B5   (B5)   *Play 8 times*

Verse 3

w/riff 1 *(x4)*
If your thing is gone and you want to ride on, cocaine.

Don't forget this fact, you can't get back, cocaine.

        C#   **B**   **A G# N.C.**
She don't   lie, she don't   lie, she don't lie,   cocaine.

Link 3

C#5 C#5 B5 C#5   B5   (B5)

Outro

        C#   **B**   **A G# N.C.**
She don't lie, she don't lie, she don't lie,   cocaine.

C#5 C#5 B5 C#5   B5   (B5)

   Repeat to fade

*Come On In My Kitchen

Words & Music by
Robert Johnson

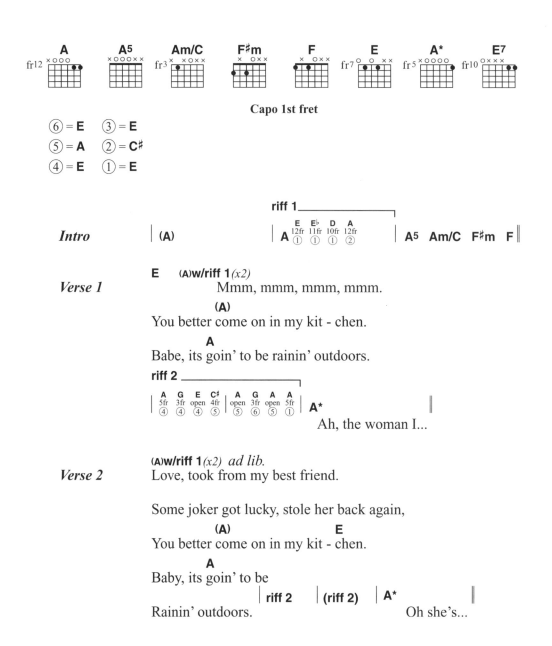

Capo 1st fret

⑥ = **E**   ③ = **E**
⑤ = **A**   ② = **C♯**
④ = **E**   ① = **E**

Intro | (A) | A | A5 Am/C F♯m F ‖

Verse 1

E   (A)w/**riff 1** *(x2)*
   Mmm, mmm, mmm, mmm.

  (A)
You better come on in my kit - chen.

   A
Babe, its goin' to be rainin' outdoors.

riff 2

     A*
      Ah, the woman I...

Verse 2

(A)w/**riff 1** *(x2) ad lib.*
Love, took from my best friend.

Some joker got lucky, stole her back again,
    (A)   E
You better come on in my kit - chen.

   A
Baby, its goin' to be

    | **riff 2** | (**riff 2**) | A*
Rainin' outdoors.   Oh she's...

Verse 3

(A)w/riff 1 *(x2)* *ad lib.*
Gone, I know she won't come back.

I've taken the last nickel out of her nation sack.
   (A)   **E**
You better come on in my kit - chen.
   A
Baby, its goin' to be
      | **riff 2** | **(riff 2)** ‖
Rainin' outdoors.

Bridge

   A*
Oh, can't you hear that wind howl 'n' all?

Oh, can't you hear that wind would howl?
   (A)   **E**
You better come on in my kit - chen.
    A
Babe, its goin' to be
     | **riff 2** | **(riff 2)** | **A***   ‖
Rainin' outdoors.   When a woman gets in...

Verse 4

(A)w/riff 1
Trouble, ev'rybody throws her down.
     E7   **A**
Lookin' for her good friend, none can be found.
           E
You better come on in my kit - chen.
    A
Babe, its goin' to be
     | **riff 2** | **(riff 2)** | **A***   ‖
Rainin' outdoors.   Winter time's co -

Verse 5

(A)w/riff 1 *(x2)* *ad lib.*
- min', it's goin' to be slow.

You can't make the winter babe, that's dry long so.
   (A)   **E**
You better come on in my kit - chen,
    A
'Cause its goin' to be
     | **riff 2** | **(riff 2)** ‖
Rainin' outdoors.

*Crosscut Saw

Words & Music by
Tony Hollins

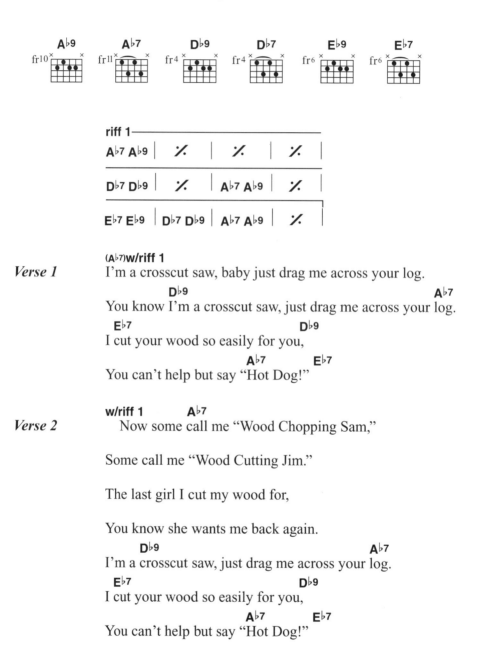

Verse 1

(A♭7)w/riff 1
I'm a crosscut saw, baby just drag me across your log.
     D♭9   **A♭7**
You know I'm a crosscut saw, just drag me across your log.
 E♭7   **D♭9**
I cut your wood so easily for you,
                      A♭7   **E♭7**
You can't help but say "Hot Dog!"

Verse 2

w/riff 1   **A♭7**
  Now some call me "Wood Chopping Sam,"

Some call me "Wood Cutting Jim."

The last girl I cut my wood for,

You know she wants me back again.
     D♭9   **A♭7**
I'm a crosscut saw, just drag me across your log.
 E♭7   **D♭9**
I cut your wood so easily for you,
                      A♭7   **E♭7**
You can't help but say "Hot Dog!"

Instr.	‖: (A♭7)w/riff 1 A♭7	A♭7	A♭7	
	D♭9 D♭9	A♭7	A♭7	
	E♭7 D♭9	A♭7	A♭7 E♭7 :‖

Verse 3

(A♭7)w/riff 1
I got a double bladed axe, that really cuts good,

Well, I'm a crosscut saw, just bury me in your wood.
     D♭9   A♭7
I'm a crosscut saw, baby just drag me across your log.
   E♭7   D♭9
I cut your wood so easily for you woman,
                      A♭7   E♭7
You can't help but say "Hot Dog!" Now watch this.

Outro

As Instr. *To fade*

Crossroads

Words & Music by
Robert Johnson

Allready clong

Chords: A   D7   E   D   E7

Intro

| A | A | A | A | D7 | D7 |

| A | A | E | D | A | A ||

Verse 1

     A
I went down to the crossroads,
D   **A**
  Fell down on my knees.
D
Down to the crossroads,
         A
Fell down on my knees.
E7
  Asked the Lord above for mercy,
D7   **A**
  Take me if you please.

Verse 2

     A
I went down to the crossroads,
D   **A**
  Tried to flag a ride.
D
Down to the crossroads,
         A
Tried to flag a ride.
   E7
Nobody seemed to know me,
D7   **A**
Everybody passed me by.

Verse 3

    A
Well I'm going down to Rosedale,

D   **A**
 Take my rider by my side.

D
Going down to Rosedale,

       A
Take my rider by my side.

    E⁷
We can still barrel-house, baby,

D⁷   **A**
 On the riverside.

Solo 1

|: A | D | A | A | D | D |

| A | A | E⁷ | D⁷ | A | A E :|

Verse 4 As Verse 3

Solo 2

|: A | A | A | A | D | D |

| A | A | E⁷ | D⁷ | A | A E :|

Play 3 times

    A
Verse 5 You can run, you can run,

D   **A**
 Tell my friend Boy Willy Brown.

D
Run, you can run,

        A
Tell my friend Boy Willy Brown,

    E⁷
That I'm standing at the crossroads,

 D⁷ **N.C.**   **A**
Believe I'm sinking down.

*Damn Right, I've Got The Blues

Words & Music by
Buddy Guy

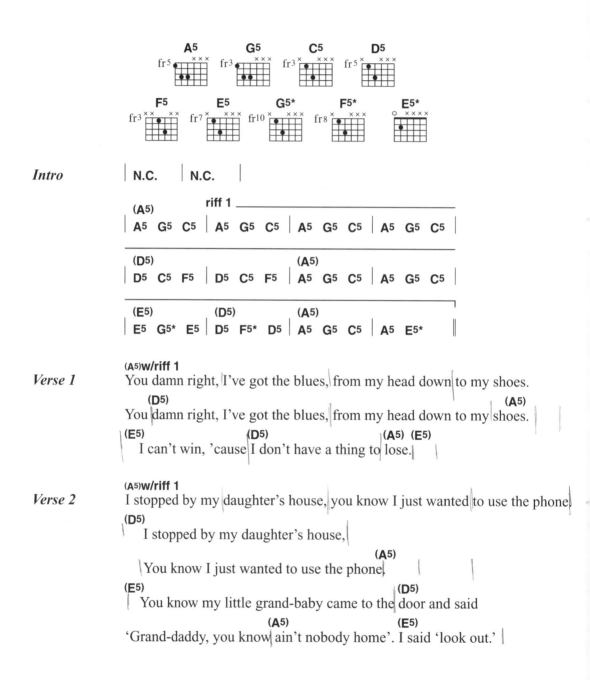

Intro | N.C. | N.C. |

(A5) riff 1 _____
| A5 G5 C5 | A5 G5 C5 | A5 G5 C5 | A5 G5 C5 |

_____
(D5)   **(A5)**
| D5 C5 F5 | D5 C5 F5 | A5 G5 C5 | A5 G5 C5 |

_____
(E5)   **(D5)**   **(A5)**
| E5 G5* E5 | D5 F5* D5 | A5 G5 C5 | A5 E5* ‖

(A5)w/riff 1
Verse 1
You damn right, I've got the blues, from my head down to my shoes.
  (D5)   **(A5)**
You damn right, I've got the blues, from my head down to my shoes.
(E5)   **(D5)**   **(A5) (E5)**
  I can't win, 'cause I don't have a thing to lose.

(A5)w/riff 1
Verse 2
I stopped by my daughter's house, you know I just wanted to use the phone
(D5)
  I stopped by my daughter's house,

                                        (A5)
You know I just wanted to use the phone
(E5)   **(D5)**
  You know my little grand-baby came to the door and said
                (A5)   **(E5)**
'Grand-daddy, you know ain't nobody home'. I said 'look out.'

Instr. 1

| | (A5)w/riff 1 | A5 | | A5 | | A5 | |
| |

	(A5)w/**riff 1**	A5	A5	A5
D5	D5	A5	A5
E5	D5	A5	A5 E5	

Verse 3

(A5)w/**riff 1**

You damn right, I've got the blues,

From my head down to my shoes.

(D5)
You damn right, I've got the blues,

(A5)
From my head down to my shoes.

(E5)　　　　　　　　　　　　　　　　**(D5)**
You know I can't win now people,

　　　　　　　　　　　　　(A5)　　　　**(E5)**
'Cause I don't have a thing to lose. Al - right.

Play 7 times

Instr. 2

‖: A5 G5 C5 | A5 G5 C5 | A5 G5 C5 | A5 G5 C5 :‖

| A5 G5 C5 ‖

Outro

A5　　　　　G5　　　　　C5　　　　A5 G5 C5
You damn right, I've got the blues.
A5　　　　　G5　　　　　C5　　　　A5 G5 C5
You damn right, I've got the blues.
A5　　　　　G5　　　　　C5　　　　A5 G5 C5
You damn right, I've got the blues.
A5　　　　　G5　　　　　C5　　　　A5 G5 C5
You damn right, I've got the blues.

‖: A5 G5 C5 | A5 G5 C5 :‖ *Repeat to fade*
　Yeah *1° only*

49

Devil Got My Woman

Words & Music by
Nehemiah James

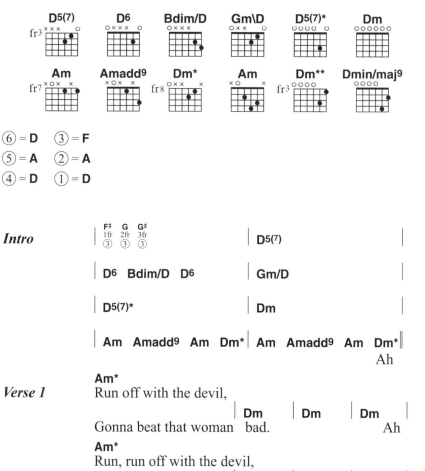

Verse 3

Am*
Laid down last night, laid down last night,

I laid down last night,
      | **Dm** | **Dm** | **Dm** |
Tryin' to take my rest.   My

Am*
Mind got to ramblin',
             | **Dm** |
Like a wild geese from the west, from the west.
| **Dm** | **Dm**   ‖
            The...

Verse 4

Am*
Woman I love, woman that I love,

Woman I love,
        | **Dm** | **Dm** | **Dm** |
Took her from my best friend.   But

Am* | **Dm** | **Dm** | **Dm** |
He got lucky, stoled her back again.   And

Am* | **Dm** | **Dm**   ‖
He got lucky, stoled her back again.

Outro | **Dm**** | **Dm/maj⁹** | **Dm** | **Dm**   ‖

Devil Take My Soul

Words & Music by
Timothy Gordine & Benjamin Darvill

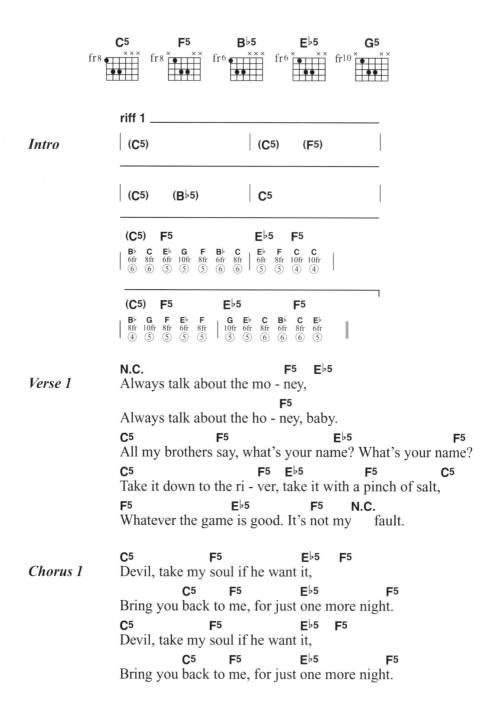

riff 1 _____

Intro

| (C5) | | (C5) (F5) |

| (C5) (B♭5) | C5 |

(C5) F5   E♭5 F5

(C5) F5   E♭5   F5

Verse 1

    N.C.   F5   E♭5
Always talk about the mo - ney,

                           F5
Always talk about the ho - ney, baby.

C5   F5   E♭5   F5
All my brothers say, what's your name? What's your name?

C5   F5   E♭5   F5   C5
Take it down to the ri - ver, take it with a pinch of salt,

F5   E♭5   F5   N.C.
Whatever the game is good. It's not my   fault.

Chorus 1

C5   F5   E♭5   F5
Devil, take my soul if he want it,

        C5   F5   E♭5   F5
Bring you back to me, for just one more night.

C5   F5   E♭5   F5
Devil, take my soul if he want it,

        C5   F5   E♭5   F5
Bring you back to me, for just one more night.

| **Link 1** | | C5 | F5 | | E♭5 | F5 | | C5 | F5 | | E♭5 | F5 | | ‖ |

w/riff 1

Verse 2

        C5   F5   E♭5
Well, I made a deal with your mamma,
                             F5
I made a deal with your pa.
        C5   F5   E♭5   F5
We   can make a deal baby like, must be hard.
        C5   F5 E♭5   F5
Go   down to the val - ley,   go down in the field.
C5   F5   E♭5   F5
Somebody come save me, please, please, I'm begging you.

Chorus 2   As Chorus 1

Link 2   ‖: As Link 1 :‖

Middle | N.C. | N.C. | N.C. | N.C. |

        | C5 F5 | E♭5   F5 | C5 F5 | E♭5 G5 | ‖
            Can   we make a deal?   Oh, oh, oh, oh.

Chorus 3

        C5   F5   E♭5   F5
‖: Devil, take my soul if he want   it,
             C5   F5   E♭5   F5
Bring you back to me, for just one more night.
C5   F5   E♭5   F5
Devil, take my soul if he want it,
             C5   F5   E♭5   F5
Bring you back to me, for just one more night. :‖

Link 3   As Link 2

Outro | N.C. | N.C. | N.C. | N.C. | ‖

Diddie Wah Diddie

*Words & Music by
Blind Blake*

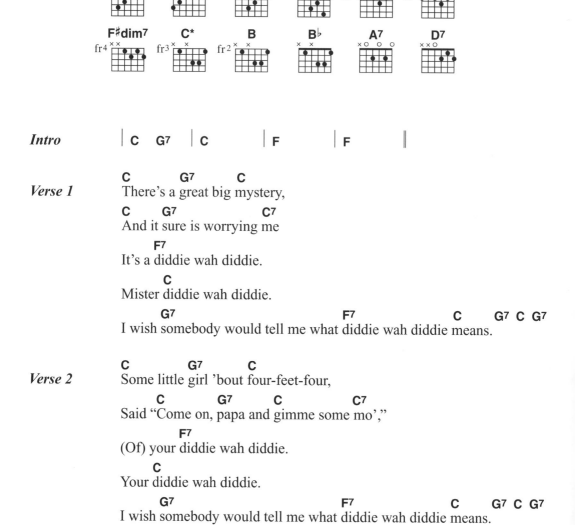

Intro | C G7 | C | F | F   ‖

Verse 1
C   G7   C
There's a great big mystery,
C   G7   C7
And it sure is worrying me
      F7
It's a diddie wah diddie.
         C
Mister diddie wah diddie.
         G7   F7   C   G7 C G7
I wish somebody would tell me what diddie wah diddie means.

Verse 2
C   G7   C
Some little girl 'bout four-feet-four,
        C   G7   C   C7
Said "Come on, papa and gimme some mo',"
         F7
(Of) your diddie wah diddie.
         C
Your diddie wah diddie.
         G7   F7   C   G7 C G7
I wish somebody would tell me what diddie wah diddie means.

Verse 3
      C   G7   C
I went out and walked around,
      C   G7   C   C7
Somebody yelled,"Now look who's in town?"
         F7
Mister diddie wah diddie.
         C
Mister diddie wah diddie.
        G7   F7   C   G7 C G7
I wish somebody would tell me what diddie wah diddie means.

Link 1
‖: C G7 | C | C G7 | C |

| F3(7) | F3(7) | C | C |

| G7 | G7 | C G7 | C G7 :‖

Verse 4
      C   G♯7   C
I went to church, put my hat on the seat,
        C   G♯7   C
A lady sat on it and said, "Daddy, you sho' is sweet,"
         F7
Mister diddie wah diddie.
         C
Mister diddie wah diddie.
        G7*   G♯7   G7*   C   G7 C G7
I wish somebody would tell me what diddie wah diddie means.

Link 2   As Link 1

Verse 5

          C   G♯7   C
I said, "Sister, I'll soon be gone,
          C   G♯7   C
Just give me that thing you sitting on,"
          F7
My diddie wah diddie.
          C
My diddie wah diddie.
          G7*   G♯7   G7*   C   G7 C G7
I wish somebody would tell me what diddie wah diddie means.

Link 3

| C G7 | C | C G7 | C C7 |
| F7 | F♯dim7 | C* B B♭ | A7 |
| D7 | G7 | C N.C. | (C)   ‖

Verse 6

          C   G7   C
Then I got put out of the church,
          C   G7   C
'Cause I talked about diddie wah diddie too much.
          F7
Mister diddie wah diddie.
          C
Mister diddie wah diddie.
          G7*   G♯7 G7*   C
I wish somebody would tell me what diddie wah diddie means.

✳ Dodo Blues

Words & Music by
C.W. Stoneking

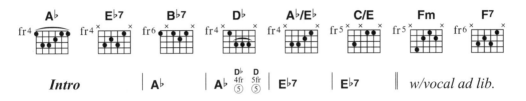

Intro | A♭ | A♭ D♭(4fr⑤) D(5fr⑤) | E♭7 | E♭7 ‖ *w/vocal ad lib.*

(ad lib.)

(E♭7)
Hey Bob, hey Bob!

What's that ol' bird you've got up there in that cage?
A♭
Bbbb... this here is ol' dodo bird.

A dodo bird?

B♭7
Ain't you never heard of a dodo bird before?
E♭7
No, I never seen one before.
A♭
That makes this the last one in existence.

The last one in where?

The last one in the world, see?

E♭7
So what are you doing with it then?
A♭
Look… I'm just trying to make some money …
B♭7
'Cause you see this here is or an ol' singin' dodo bird.

That's a singin' dodo bird hey?

That's right.

So what you doing down there, ol' dodo bird?
A♭
Well I'm just sitting on this …

E♭7
I'm just sitting on this cage, gonna sing a tune.

Well, let's hear it then…

Verse 1

$A\flat$ $B\flat7$
Nothing, nothing can be right, when ev'rything is wrong.
$E\flat7$
Nothing can be wrong when I'm walking with my baby,
$A\flat$ $E\flat7$
I weak and I worn I said,
$A\flat$ $B\flat7$
Nothing, nothing can be right, when ev'rything is wrong.
   $E\flat7$
No - thing can be wrong when I'm walking with my baby,
$A\flat$ $E\flat7$
I weak and I worn.

Bridge 1

$D\flat$ $B\flat7$ $A\flat/E\flat$
 My baby quit me for a long, tall, handsome man,
         C/E Fm
With something   I ain't got.
$D\flat$ $A\flat/E\flat$ $F7$
 Nothing can be wrong when I'm walking with my ba - by,
$B\flat7$ **N.C.** $E\flat7$
 When I'm not I feel so lonesome.

Verse 2

$A\flat$ $B\flat7$
 Nothing, nothing can be right, when ev'rything is wrong.
$E\flat7$
Nothing can be wrong when I'm walking with my baby,
$A\flat$ $E\flat7$
I weak and I worn, I said,
$A\flat$ $B\flat7$
 Nothing, nothing, nothing can be right. That ol' daughter…

It sounds like you got too much bad luck man.
      $E\flat7$
I sure know, I got bad luck an' misery.
           $A\flat$
I'd sure like have an egg, ol' dodo bird.
    $E\flat7$
Give me five dollars for this ol' bird, now look here…

Bridge 2

$D\flat$ $B\flat7$ $A\flat/E\flat$ C/E   Fm
Anytime that I telephone, she don't return my call.

$D\flat$ $A\flat/E\flat$ F7 $B\flat7$ N.C. $E\flat7$
If I can't smile when I feel blue, then I never smile at all.

Be-bopper day boo…

Verse 3

$A\flat$ $B\flat7$
Nothing, nothing can be right, when ev'rything is wrong.

$E\flat7$
Nothing can be wrong when I'm walking with my baby,

$A\flat$ $E\flat7$
I weak and I worn,   I said,

$A\flat$ $B\flat7$
Nothing, nothing can be right, when ev'rything is wrong.

    $E\flat7$
No - thing can be wrong when I'm walking with my baby,

$A\flat$ N.C. $E\flat7$ N.C. $A\flat$ $A\flat$
I   weak   and I worn, woh - oo, woh - oo, woh - oo, woh, oh Lord…

Dog House Boogie

Words & Music by
Steve Wold

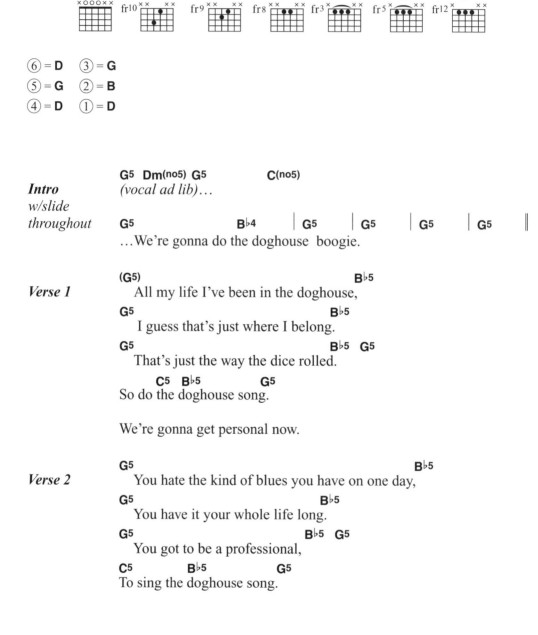

Intro
w/slide
throughout

| G5 | Dm(no5) | G5 | | C(no5) |

(vocal ad lib)…

| G5 | | B♭4 | G5 | G5 | G5 | G5 |

…We're gonna do the doghouse boogie.

Verse 1

(G5)   B♭5
    All my life I've been in the doghouse,
G5   B♭5
    I guess that's just where I belong.
G5   B♭5   G5
    That's just the way the dice rolled.
    C5   B♭5   G5
So do the doghouse song.

We're gonna get personal now.

Verse 2

G5   B♭5
    You hate the kind of blues you have on one day,
G5   B♭5
    You have it your whole life long.
G5   B♭5   G5
    You got to be a professional,
C5   B♭5   G5
To sing the doghouse song.

Chorus 1

G5   C5   B♭5 G5
  A-whoo, yeah, yeah, yeah.
G5   C5   B♭5 G5
  A-whoo, yeah, yeah, yeah.
G5   C5   B♭5 G5
  A-whoo, yeah, yeah, yeah.
C5   B♭5   G5* | G5* |
Sing the doghouse song.
            B♭5 C5 B♭5 G5 B♭5 C5 B♭5 G5
The dog - house,
            B♭5 C5 B♭5 G5 B♭5 C5 B♭5 G5
The dog - house,
            B♭5 C5 B♭5 G5 B♭5 C5 B♭5 G5
The dog - house,
C5   B♭5   G5
Do the doghouse song.

Verse 3

(G5)
I'm gonna tell you my story.
                                              B♭5 G5
My mum and dad broke up when I was four years old,

When I was seven, she went and got herself another man,
          B♭5   G5
It was hell   y'all.
                                  B♭5 G5
I left home when I was fourteen years of age,
                           B♭5 G5
I Figured I'd do better on my own.

Then followed a number of years,
                  B♭5 G5
Of bumming around and liv - ing kind of hand and mouth,
                  B♭5 G5
Sometimes getting locked up   and such,
                         B♭5 G5
And sometimes just going cold and hun - gry.
              B♭5 G5
I didn't have me no real school education,
                            B♭5 G5
So what in the hell was I gonna be able to   do?

cont.　　　　But I always did pick up the guitar

B♭5 G5

I used to put the hat out for spare change,

　　　　　　B♭5 G5

But I'm making this here record for y'all,

　　　　　　　　　　　　B♭5 G5

And I'm still trying to get your spare change.

I don't know why it went wrong,

　　　　　　B♭5 G5

It ain't bad now,　　and I just keep playing my

　　　　　B♭5 G5 C5　　　**B♭5**　　　　**G5**

Doghouse mu - sic,　　sing the doghouse song.

G5　　　　　　　　　**C5**　**B♭5**　　**G5**

Chorus 2　　A-whoo, a-whoo, yeah, yeah, yeah.

G5　　　　　　　　　**C5**　**B♭5**　　**G5**

A-whoo, a-whoo, yeah, yeah, yeah.

G5　　　　　　　　　**C5**　**B♭5**　　**G5**

A-whoo, a-whoo, yeah, yeah, yeah.

C5　　　**B♭5**　　　　**G5***　│ **G5***　　　│

Sing the doghouse song,

　　　　B♭5 C5 B♭5 G5 B♭5 C5 B♭5 G5

Dog - house,

　　　　B♭5 C5 B♭5 G5 B♭5 C5 B♭5 G5

Dog - house,

　　　　B♭5 C5 B♭5 G5 B♭5 C5 B♭5 G5

Dog - house,

C5　　　　**B♭5**　　　　　**G5***　│ **G5***　　　│

Sing the doghouse song.

　　　　B♭5 C5 B♭5 G5 B♭5 C5 B♭5 G5

Dog - house,

　　　　B♭5 C5 B♭5 G5 B♭5 C5 B♭5 G5

Dog - house,

　　　　B♭5 C5 B♭5 G5 B♭5 C5 B♭5 G5

Dog - house.

　　　C5　　　**B♭5**　　　**G5**　　**C5**　　　　　　**B♭5**　**G5**

Outro　‖: Sing the doghouse song, sing the dog - house song,

C5　　　　**B♭5**　　　**G5***　**C5**　　　　　　**B♭5**　　**G5***

Sing the doghouse song, sing the dog - house song. :‖

　　　　　　　　　　　　　　　　Repeat to fade w/slide ad lib.

Dying Crapshooter's Blues

Words & Music by
Willie McTell

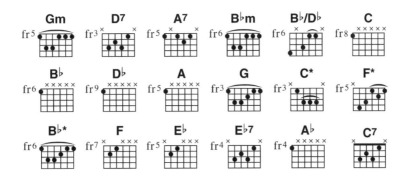

Intro

I am going to play this song that I made myself,

Originally, it's from Atlanta,

It's three different marches of tunes.

| **Gm** | **(Gm)** | **(Gm)** | **D7** |

Gm
Little Jesse was a gambler,
D7   **Gm**
Night and day he used crooked cards and dice.
                                                         D7
He was a sinful boy, good hearted but had no soul,
                                         Gm
Heart was hard and cold like ice.

Little Jesse was a wild, reckless gambler,
          D7
Won a gang of change, and a many
                                         Gm
Gambler's heart he left in pain.

                                                                         D7

Little Jesse, began to lose his money, but he was all alone,

                    Gm

And his heart had even turned to stone.

                                D7

The Police walked up and shot my friend Jesse down,

                  Gm

"Boy's I got to die to - day."

            A7

He had a gang of crapshooters and gamblers at his bedside,

                      Gm

But here are the words he had to say:

  B♭m   **B♭m/D♭**   **C B♭ Gm**

"I guess I ought to know, how   I wants to go,"

How you wanna go, Jesse?

           Gm

I want eight crapshooters for my pallbearers,

D7   **Gm**

Let them all be dressed down in black.

I want nine men going to the graveyard,

              D7   **Gm**

But only eight men comin' back.

              A7

 I want a gang of gamblers gathered round my coffin side,

                         Gm

With a crooked card printed on my hearse.

         A7 N.C.   **A7 N.C.**

Don't say the crapshooters'll ever grieve over me,

        D7 N.C.

My life been a doggone curse.

Gm

Send poker players to the graveyard,

D7   **Gm**

Dig my grave with the ace of spades,

I want twelve polices in my funeral march.

          D7   **Gm**

High   sheriff playin' black jack leading the parade.

A⁷
I want the judge and solicitor who jailed me fourteen times,
Gm
Put a pair of dice in my shoes,
B♭*
Let   a deck of cards be my tombstone,
     F   **E♭**   **D♭**   **A**   **B♭***   **B♭ A A♭ Gm**
I got the dyin' crap - shoo - ter's blues.

    Gm
I want sixteen real good crapshooters,
        D⁷
Sixteen bootleggers to sing a song,
   Gm   **D⁷**
Six - teen buck riders gambling while a couple   tend the bar
           Gm
While I'm rollin' along'.

He wanted twenty two women outta the Hampton Hotel,
          D⁷
Twenty six off of South Bell,
Gm
Twenty nine women outta North Atlanta.
    D⁷   **Gm**
Know that little Jesse didn't pass out so swell,

His head was achin', heart was thumpin',
D⁷   **Gm**
Little Jesse went down bouncin' and jumpin'.
                    D⁷
Folks, don't be standing around Jessie cryin',
           G   **C⁷**
He wants every - body to do the Charleston whilst he dyin'.
    Gm
One   foot up, a toenail dragging,
B♭*
Throw my buddy Jesse in the hoodoo wagon.
Gm   **B♭ A**   **Gm**
Come here mama with that can of booze,
               Gm   **E♭⁷**   **D⁷**
He got the dyin' crap - shooter's blues,
Gm   **C***   **F***   **B♭***
Passin' on with the dyin' crap - shooter's blues.

Dust My Blues

Words & Music by
Robert Johnson
Arranged by Elmore James

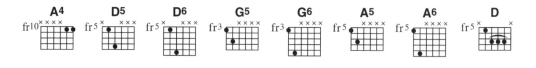

riff 1 _____

Intro | A4 | D5 D6 D5 D6 | A4 | D5 D6 D5 D6 |

| G5 G6 G5 G6 | G5 G6 G5 G6 | A4 | D5 D6 D5 D6 |

| A5 A6 A5 A6 | G5 G6 G5 G6 | D5 (D5/C /B /B♭ | /A) A5 ‖

riff 2 starts...

Verse 1
          D5   D6   D5   D6
I'm gonna get up in the morning,
 G5   G6 G5 G6   A4 | D5 D6 D5 D6 |
I believe I'll dust my blues.
         G5   G6   G5   G6
I'm gonna get up in the morning,
 G5   G6 G5 G6   A4 | D5 D6 D5 D6 |
I believe I'll dust my blues.
       A5   A6 A5   A6
I gotta leave my baby,
G5 G6   G5 G6 | D5 (D5/C /B /B♭ | /A) A5 ‖
 I ain't got no time to lose. ...riff 2 ends

w/riff 2
Verse 2
I don't want no woman, that'll treat me wrong all the time.

I don't want no woman, that'll treat me wrong all the time.

Well I'm tired of the way she treat me, I was about to lose my mind.

Verse 3

w/riff 2
I'm gonna write a letter, I better send her a telegram.

I'm gonna write a letter, I better send her a telegram.

She left me soon this morning, and she got me in an awful jam.

Instr.

| A4 | | D5 D6 D5 D6 | A4 | | D5 D6 D5 D6 |

| G5 G6 G5 G6 | G5 G6 G5 G6 | D5 D6 D5 D6 | D5 D6 D5 D6 |

| A5 A6 A5 A6 | G5 G6 G5 G6 | D5 (D5/C /B /B♭) | /A) A5 ‖

Verse 4

w/riff 1 *(x4)*
I believe, I believe my time ain't long.

G5   G6   G5   G6   G5 G6   G5   G6 | riff 1 |
I be - lieve, I be - lieve my time ain't long.

A5   A6 A5   A6
I gotta leave my baby,

G5   G6 G5   G6   D5 (D5/C /B /B♭) | /A) A5 ‖
I gotta   leave my happy home.

Instr.

| riff 1 | riff 1 | riff 1 | riff 1 |

| G5 G6 G5 G6 | G5 G6 G5 G6 | riff 1 | riff 1 |

| A5 A6 A5 A6 | G5 G6 G5 G6 | D5 (D5/C /B /B♭) | /A) D ‖

Evil (Is Going On)

Words & Music by
Willie Dixon

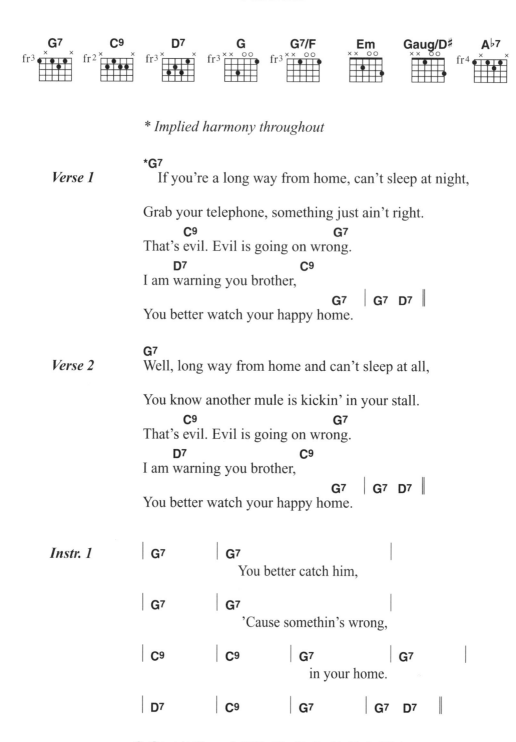

* Implied harmony throughout

Verse 1

*G7
If you're a long way from home, can't sleep at night,

Grab your telephone, something just ain't right.

C9   G7
That's evil. Evil is going on wrong.

D7   C9
I am warning you brother,

                              G7 │ G7 D7 ‖
You better watch your happy home.

Verse 2

G7
Well, long way from home and can't sleep at all,

You know another mule is kickin' in your stall.

C9   G7
That's evil. Evil is going on wrong.

D7   C9
I am warning you brother,

                              G7 │ G7 D7 ‖
You better watch your happy home.

Instr. 1   │ G7   │ G7   │
                        You better catch him,

                  │ G7   │ G7   │
                        'Cause somethin's wrong,

                  │ C9   │ C9   │ G7   │ G7   │
                                    in your home.

                  │ D7   │ C9   │ G7   │ G7 D7   ‖

Verse 3

G⁷
Well, if you call her on the telephone,

And she answers awful slow

Grab the first thing smoking if you have to hobo,

    C⁹   G⁷
That's evil. Evil is going on wrong.

    D⁷   C⁹
I am warning you brother,

                               G⁷ | G⁷ D⁷ ‖
You better watch your happy home.

Instr. 2

| G⁷ | G⁷ | G⁷ | G⁷ |

| C⁹ | C⁹ | G⁷ | G⁷ |

| D⁷ | C⁹ | G⁷ | G⁷ D⁷ ‖

Verse 4

G⁷
If you make it to your house, knock on the front door,

Run around to the back, you'll catch him just before he goes.

    C⁹   G⁷
That's evil. Evil is going on.

    D⁷   C⁹
I am warning you brother,

                         G
You better watch your happy home.

| G⁷/F Em Gaug/D♯ | D⁷ A♭7 G⁷ ‖

Farther Up The Road

Words & Music by
Joe Veasey & Don Robey

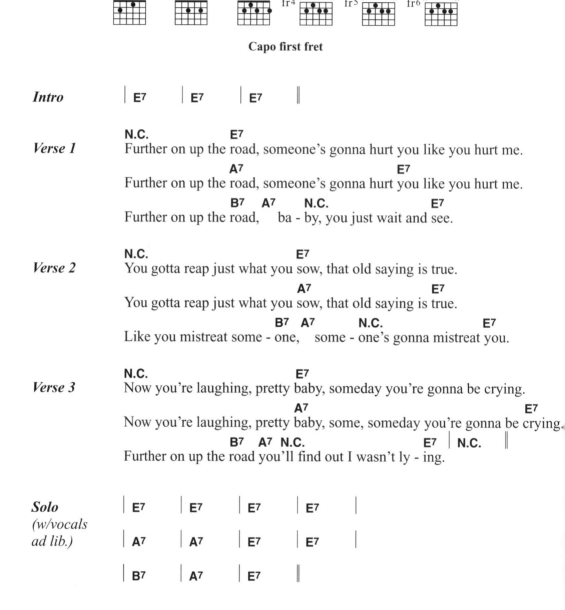

E7   A7   B7   D9   D#9   E9

Capo first fret

Intro | E7 | E7 | E7   ‖

Verse 1
N.C.   E7
Further on up the road, someone's gonna hurt you like you hurt me.
A7   E7
Further on up the road, someone's gonna hurt you like you hurt me.
B7   A7   N.C.   E7
Further on up the road,   ba - by, you just wait and see.

Verse 2
N.C.   E7
You gotta reap just what you sow, that old saying is true.
A7   E7
You gotta reap just what you sow, that old saying is true.
B7   A7   N.C.   E7
Like you mistreat some - one,   some - one's gonna mistreat you.

Verse 3
N.C.   E7
Now you're laughing, pretty baby, someday you're gonna be crying.
A7   E7
Now you're laughing, pretty baby, some, someday you're gonna be crying.
B7   A7 N.C.   E7 | N.C.   ‖
Further on up the road you'll find out I wasn't ly - ing.

Solo
(w/vocals
ad lib.)
| E7 | E7 | E7 | E7 |
| A7 | A7 | E7 | E7 |
| B7 | A7 | E7   ‖

Verse 4

N.C.   E⁷
Further on up the road, when you're all alone and blue.

         A⁷   E⁷
Further on up the road, when you're all alone and blue.

               B⁷   A⁷
You're gonna ask me to take you back baby,

N.C.   E⁷ | E⁷   ‖
But I'll have somebody new.

Outro

| E⁷ | E⁷ | E⁷ | E⁷ |
| A⁷ | A⁷ | E⁷ | E⁷ |
| B⁷ | A⁷ | E⁷ | E⁷ D⁹ D♯9 E⁹ ‖

The First Time I Met The Blues

Words & Music by
Eurreal Montgomery

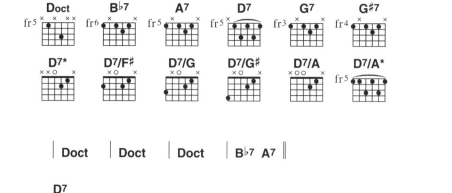

Intro | Doct | Doct | Doct | B♭7 A7 ‖

Verse 1

D7
The first time I met the blues,

G7   **D7**
People, you know I was walkin', I was walkin' down through the woods.

      G7
Yes, the first time, the first time I met you, blues,

                                          D7
Blues you know I was walkin', I was walkin' down through the woods.

      A7   **G♯7**
Yes, I've watched my house burnin' blues,

G7
Blues, you know you done me, you done me,

           D7
All the harm that you could.

Verse 2

     D7
The blues got after me,

G7   **D7**
People, you know they ran me from tree to tree.

      G7
Yes, the blues got after me,

                               D7
Blues, you know you ran me, ran me from tree to tree.

      A7   **G♯7**
Yes, you should-a heard me beg ya, blues,

     G7   **D7**
Ah,   blues, don't murder me.

Verse 3

D7
Yes, good mornin' blues,

G7   **D7**
Blues, I wonder, I wonder what you're doin' here so soon.

    G7
Yes, good mornin', good mornin', good mornin', mister blues,

                                                                        D7
Blues, I wonder, I keep wonderin' what you're doin' here so soon.

        A7   **G♯7**   **G7**
Yes, you know you'll be with me every mornin', blues,

N.C.   **D7* D7/F♯ D7/G D7/G♯**│ **D7/A B♭7 D7/A*** ‖
Every night and every noon.

Give It Up Or Let Me Go

Words & Music by
Bonnie Raitt

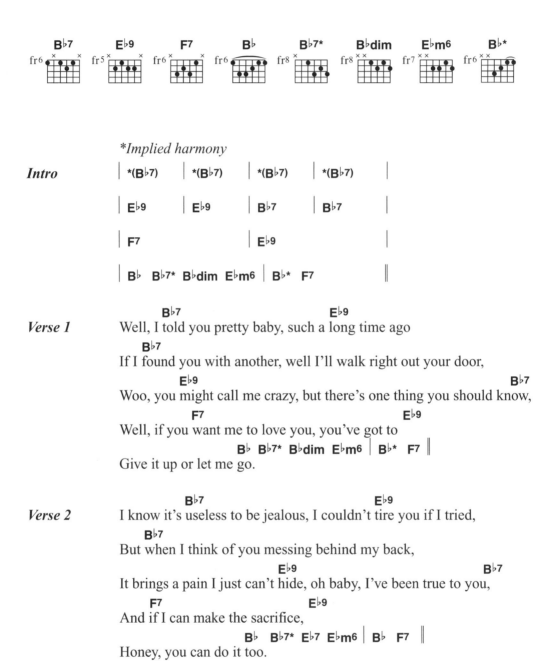

Bb7	Eb9	F7	Bb	Bb7*	Bbdim	Ebm6	Bb*
fr6	fr5	fr6	fr6	fr8	fr8	fr7	fr6

Implied harmony

Intro | *(Bb7) | *(Bb7) | *(Bb7) | *(Bb7) |

| Eb9 | Eb9 | Bb7 | Bb7 |

| F7 | Eb9 |

| Bb Bb7* Bbdim Ebm6 | Bb* F7 ‖

Verse 1

     Bb7   Eb9
Well, I told you pretty baby, such a long time ago

   Bb7
If I found you with another, well I'll walk right out your door,

      Eb9   Bb7
Woo, you might call me crazy, but there's one thing you should know,

        F7   Eb9
Well, if you want me to love you, you've got to

               Bb Bb7* Bbdim Ebm6 | Bb* F7 ‖
Give it up or let me go.

Verse 2

       Bb7   Eb9
I know it's useless to be jealous, I couldn't tire you if I tried,

   Bb7
But when I think of you messing behind my back,

         Eb9   Bb7
It brings a pain I just can't hide, oh baby, I've been true to you,

      F7   Eb9
And if I can make the sacrifice,

           Bb Bb7* Eb7 Ebm6 | Bb F7 ‖
Honey, you can do it too.

Instr. 1

B♭7	E♭9	B♭7	B♭7	
E♭9	E♭9	B♭7	B♭7	
F7	E♭9	B♭ B♭7* B♭dim E♭m6	B♭* F7 ‖

Verse 3

       B♭7   **N.C**
Well, you come home drunk and nasty,
       E♭9 N.C
You won't tell me where you been,
B♭7 N.C   **E♭9**
Just when things are nice and sweet, you goin' back out a - gain.
               B♭7
Why do you wanna mess up a good thing?
       F7   **E♭9**
I'm gonna find me another man,
              B♭ B♭7* B♭dim E♭m6 | **B♭ F7** ‖
One who wants to give me ev - erything.

Instr. 2   As Instr. 1

Verse 4   As Verse 1

w/vocal ad lib.

Instr. 3

‖: B♭7	E♭9	B♭7	B♭7	
E♭9	E♭9	B♭7	B♭7	
F7	E♭9	B♭ B♭7* E♭7 E♭m6	B♭ F7 :‖
B♭7 (⌢)	‖

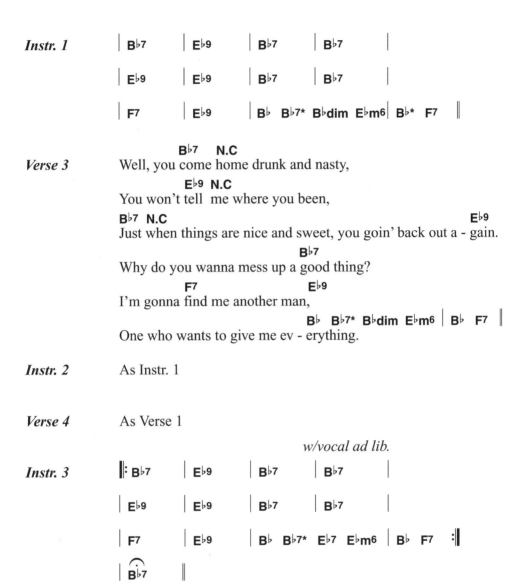

Good Morning Little Schoolgirl

Words & Music by
B. Level & B. Love

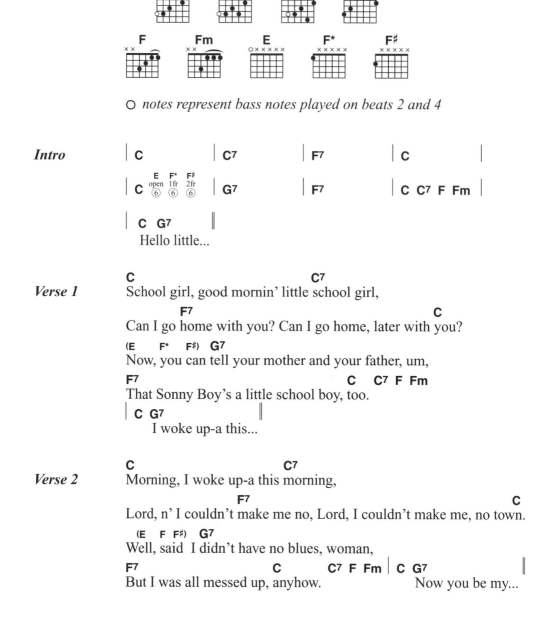

○ *notes represent bass notes played on beats 2 and 4*

Intro

| C | C7 | F7 | C |

| C E F* F# open 1fr 2fr ⑥ ⑥ ⑥ | G7 | F7 | C C7 F Fm |

| C G7 ‖

Hello little...

Verse 1

C   C7
School girl, good mornin' little school girl,

      F7   C
Can I go home with you? Can I go home, later with you?

(E   F*   F#) **G7**
Now, you can tell your mother and your father, um,

F7   C C7 F Fm
That Sonny Boy's a little school boy, too.

| C G7 ‖

     I woke up-a this...

Verse 2

C   C7
Morning, I woke up-a this morning,

      F7   C
Lord, n' I couldn't make me no, Lord, I couldn't make me, no town.

(E F F#) **G7**
Well, said I didn't have no blues, woman,

F7   C   C7 F Fm | C G7 ‖
But I was all messed up, anyhow.   Now you be my...

Verse 3

    C   **C7**
Baby, mmm, come on an' be my baby, mmm.

              F7   **C**
I'll buy you a diamond, I'll buy you a diamond ring.

    (E   F F♯)   **G7
Well, if you don't be my little woman,

    F7   **C**   **C7 F Fm**
Then I won't buy you a doggone thing.

 | **C G7** ||
      I'm gonna buy me a...

Verse 4

    C   **C7**
Airplane, I'm gonna buy me a air - plane.

                   F7
I'm goin' fly all over this land,

                            C
I'm goin' fly all over this land's town.

    (E   F F♯)   **G7
Don't find the woman that I'm lovin',

    F7   **C**   **C7 F Fm** | **C G7** ||
Then I ain't goin' to let my airplane down.

Instr.

 | **C** | **C7** | **F7** | **C** |

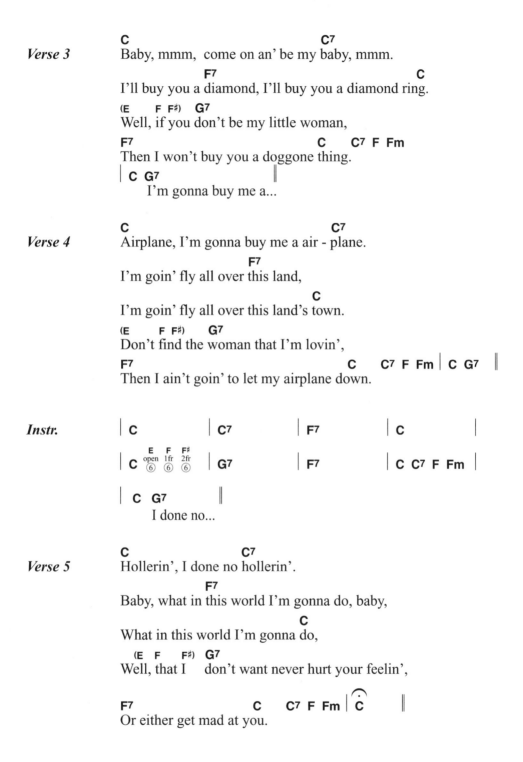

 | **C** | **G7** | **F7** | **C C7 F Fm** |

 | **C G7** ||
      I done no...

Verse 5

    C   **C7**
Hollerin', I done no hollerin'.

                   F7
Baby, what in this world I'm gonna do, baby,

                       C
What in this world I'm gonna do,

    (E F   F♯) **G7
Well, that I   don't want never hurt your feelin',

    F7   **C**   **C7 F Fm** | ⌢ **C** ||
Or either get mad at you.

Hellhound On My Trail

Words & Music by
Robert Johnson

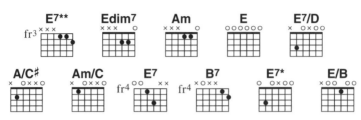

⑥ = E   ③ = G♯

⑤ = B   ② = B

④ = E   ① = E

Intro | E7**   Edim7 $\frac{2}{4}$| Am $\frac{4}{4}$| E   E7/D   A/C♯   Am/C | E7   ‖

                       E
Verse 1   I got to keep movin'

                B7
            I got to keep movin',

                          E
Blues fallin' down like hail,

E7*   A/C♯   Am/C | E7 | E7 | E7*   ‖
Blues fall - in' down like hail.   Mmm.

Blues fallin' down like hail,

         A/C♯   Am/C | E   E7*   A/C♯|
Blues fallin' down   like hail.

E7   B7
   And the day,   it keeps on worryin' me,

It's a hellhound on my trail,

E   E7/D   A/C♯   Am/C E   E7/D
  Hellhound on my trail,

A/C♯   Am/C | E7 | E7   ‖
Hellhound on my trail.

Verse 2

(E7)   E
If to - day was Christmas Eve,

B7
If to - day was Christmas Eve,

              | E E7/D A/C♯ E7 |
And tomorrow was Christmas Day,

(E7)
If today was Christmas Eve,

And tomorrow was Christmas Day,

   A/C♯   Am/C   E7
Oh, wouldn't we have a time, baby?

        B7
All I would need, my little sweet rider,

Just to pass the time away.

E7/D   A/C♯ Am/C E   E7/D   A/C♯   Am/C
  Huh, huh,   to pass the time   away.

| E/B | E7 ||

Verse 3

(E7)   E
You sprinkled   hot foot powder, mmm,

             E7/D   A/C♯   Am/C | E/B E7 |
Around my door, all around   my door.

You sprinkled hot foot powder,

                        E7/D A/C♯ Am/C | E/B E7 |
All 'round your daddy's door. Hmm, hmm, hmm.

            B7
It keep me with a ramblin' mind, rider,

              E
Ev'ry old place I go,

   E7/D   A/C♯ Am/C | E E7/D A/C♯ Am/C | E7 ||
Ev'ry   old place I go.

Verse 4

(E7)   E
    I can tell the wind is risin', the leaves tremblin' on the tree,

                     E7/D A/C♯ Am/C | E/B E7 |
Tremblin' on the tree.

I can tell the wind is risin',

Leaves tremblin' on the tree.
E7/D   A/C♯ Am/C | E/B E E7 |
Hmm, hmm, hmm.

     B7
All I need's my little sweet woman and to keep my company.

E   E7/D A/C♯ Am/C | E E7/D A/C♯ Am/C |
  Hey,   my company.

| Am/C E7 | E7 ||

Mannish Boy

Words & Music by
McKinley Morganfield, Ellas McDaniels & Melvin London

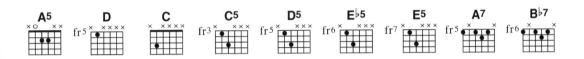

Intro
(Freely
vocal ad lib.)

Ooooooh, yeah, ooh, yeah

Everythin', everythin', everythin' gonna be alright this mornin'

Ooh yeah, whoa.

riff 1

| A5 D A5 C A5 |

w/riff 1 throughout

Verse 1

Now when I was a young boy, at the age of five,

My mother said I was gonna be, the greatest man alive.

But now I'm a man, way past 21,

I want you to believe me baby, I had lots of fun.

I'm a man, I spell M,

A child, N.

That represents man, no B,

O child, Y.

Chorus 1

w/riff 1 throughout
That mean mannish boy, I'm a man.

I'm a full grown man, I'm a man.

I'm a natural born lovers man, I'm a man.

I'm a rollin' stone, I'm a man.

I'm a hoochie coochie man.

Verse 2

w/riff 1 throughout
Sittin' on the outside, just me and my mate.

You know I'm made to move you honey, come up two hours late.

Wasn't that a man, I spell M,

A child, N.

That represents man, no B,

O child, Y.

Chorus 2

w/riff 1 throughout
That mean mannish boy, I'm a man.

I'm a full grown man, man.

I'm a natural born lovers man, man.

I'm a rollin' stone, man-child.

I'm a hoochie coochie man.

| | **w/riff 1 throughout** |
| *Verse 3* | The line I shoot, and I'll never miss, |

The line I shoot, and I'll never miss,

When I make love to a woman, she can't resist.

I think I go down, to old Kansas Stew,

I'm gonna bring back my second cousin, that little Johnny Cockeroo.

All you little girls, sittin'out at that line,

I can make love to you woman, in five minutes time.

Ain't that a man, I spell M,

A child, N.

That represents I'm grown, no B,

O child, Y.

w/riff 1 throughout

Chorus 3 That mean mannish boy, man.

I'm a full grown man, man.

I'm a natural born lovers man,

Man, I'm a rollin' stone.

I'm a man-child,

I'm a hoochie coochie man.

w/riff 1 throughout

Chorus 3 Well, well, well, well,

Hurry, hurry, hurry, hurry.

Don't hurt me, don't hurt me child,

Don't hurt me, don't hurt me, don't hurt me child.

Well, well, well, well.

Outro | A5 C5 D5 E♭5 E | B♭7 A7 ‖

*Help Me

Words & Music by
Willie Dixon, Sonny Boy Williamson & Ralph Bass

Chords: F5, A♭5, B♭5, B♭5*, D♭5, E♭5, C5, F5*, Fm, B♭m, C7

riff 1 _____

Intro

| F5 A♭5 B♭5 | F5 A♭5 B♭5 | F5 A♭5 B♭5 | F5 A♭5 B♭5 |

| B♭5* D♭5 E♭5 | B♭5* D♭5 E♭5 | F5 A♭5 B♭5 | F5 A♭5 B♭5 |

| C5 E♭5 F5* | B♭5* D♭5 E♭5 | F5 A♭5 B♭5 | F5 A♭5 B♭5 ‖

Verse 1

(Fm)w/riff 1
You got to help me, I can't do it all by myself.
(B♭m)   (Fm)
You got to help me baby, I can't do it all by myself.
                        (C7)
You know if you don't help me darling,
(B♭m)   (Fm)
I'll have to find myself somebody else.

Verse 2

(Fm)w/riff 1
I may have to wash, I may have to sew,

I may have to cook, I might mop the floor.
(B♭m)   (Fm)
But you help me baby.
                (C7)
You know if you don't help me darling,
(B♭m)   (Fm)
I'll find myself somebody else.

Link 1   As Intro

Verse 3

(Fm)w/**riff 1**
|When I walk,|you walk with me,|when I talk,|you talk to me.|
   (B♭m)   (Fm)
|Oh baby, I can't|do it all by myself| |
                (C7)
|You know, if you|don't help me darling,
         (B♭m)   (Fm)
I'll have to |find myself somebody |else.

Help me, |help me darling. |

Link 2   As Intro

Verse 4

(Fm)w/**riff 1**
|Bring my nightshirt, |put on your |morning gown. |Whoo,
          (B♭m)   (Fm)
Bring my |nightshirt, |put on your morning |gown. |
           (C7)
|Darlin', I|know we ain't sleeping,|
(B♭m)   (Fm)
|But I just feel like lying|down. Oh yeah.| |

Outro   As Intro   *To fade*

Hey Joe

Words & Music by
Billy Roberts

E   Em⁷   F♯5/E   C   G   D   A

(1 bar count in)

Intro | N.C. Guitar fill | E Em⁷ F♯5/E | E   ‖

Verse 1

```
      C   G D        A           E              | E  |
Hey Joe, where you goin' with that gun of yours?
      C    G D   A                   E                | E  |
  Hey Joe, I said where you goin' with that gun in your hand?
      C                  G
  I'm goin' down to shoot my lady,
  D            A                                    E        | E  |
  You know I caught her messin' 'round with a - nother man.
              C              G
Yeah, I'm goin' down to shoot my ol' lady,
  D            A                           E
  You know I caught her messin' 'round with another man
```

Huh! And that ain't too cool.

Verse 2

```
      C      G D A                 E
  A-hey Joe,     I heard you shot your woman down,
```

You shot her down now.

```
      C      G D A                    E
  A-hey Joe,     I heard you shot your old lady down,
```

You shot her down in the ground, yeah!

```
  C        G
  Yes, I did, I shot her,
  D            A                    E                        | E  |
  You know I caught her messin' 'round, messin' 'round town,
        C    G
Uh, yes I did, I shot her.
```

cont.

D   A   E

You know I caught my old lady messin' 'round town,

Then I gave her the gun,

I shot her.

Guitar solo

| C   G | D   A | E | E | |

Alright, shoot her one more time again baby!

| C   G | D   A | E | E | |

Yeah! Dig it.

| C   G | D   A | E | E ‖

Oh, alright.

Verse 3

C   G

Hey Joe,

D A   E

Where you gonna run to now, where you gonna run to?

C   G

"Hey Joe", I said,

D A   E

"Where you gonna run to now, where you gonna go?"

C   G

I'm goin' way down South,

D A   E   E

Way down to Mexico way.

C   G

I'm goin' way down South,

D A   E

Way down where I can be free,

Ain't no one gonna find me.

Outro

C   G

Ain't no hang-man gonna,

D   A   E

He ain't gonna put a rope around me,

You better believe it right now,

I gotta go now,

C   G

Hey Joe,

D   A   E

You better run on down,

Goodbye everybody. Ow!   *To fade*

Hi-Heel Sneakers

Words & Music by
Robert Higgenbotham

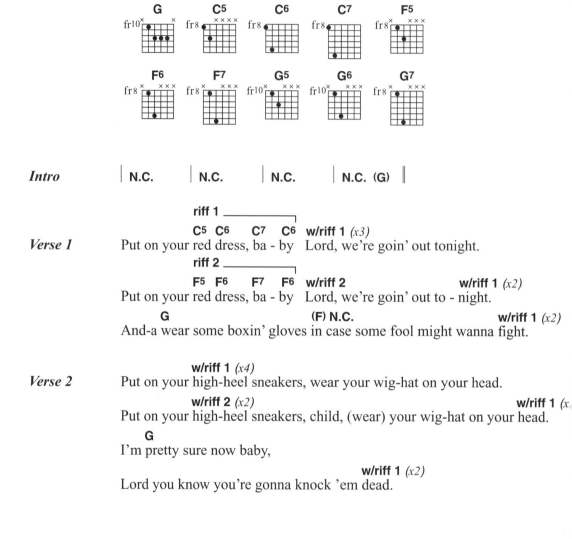

Intro | N.C. | N.C. | N.C. | N.C. (G) ‖

Verse 1

riff 1 ⌐——————⌐
C5 C6   C7   C6 w/riff 1 *(x3)*
Put on your red dress, ba - by Lord, we're goin' out tonight.

riff 2 ⌐——————⌐
F5 F6   F7   F6 w/riff 2   w/riff 1 *(x2)*
Put on your red dress, ba - by Lord, we're goin' out to - night.

G   **(F) N.C.**   w/riff 1 *(x2)*
And-a wear some boxin' gloves in case some fool might wanna fight.

Verse 2

w/riff 1 *(x4)*
Put on your high-heel sneakers, wear your wig-hat on your head.

w/riff 2 *(x2)*   w/riff 1 *(x...*
Put on your high-heel sneakers, child, (wear) your wig-hat on your head.

G
I'm pretty sure now baby,

                                w/riff 1 *(x2)*
Lord you know you're gonna knock 'em dead.

Instr. | (C) riff 1 | riff 1 | riff 1 | riff 1 |

| (F) riff 2 | riff 2 | (C) riff 1 | riff 1 |

| G5 G6 G7 G6 | (F) riff 2 | (C) riff 1 | riff 1   ‖

                                w/riff 1 *(x4)*
Verse 3   Put on your high-heel sneakers, wear your wig-hat on your head.
                        w/riff 2 *(x2)*   **w/riff 1** *(x2)*
             Put on your high-heel sneakers, wear your wig-hat on your head.
                G   **(F) N.C.**
             Ya know you're real fine,
                                                w/riff 1 *(x2)*
             I'm pretty sure you're gonna knock 'em dead.

Outro | (C) riff 1 | riff 1 |

| (F) riff 2 | G5 G6 G7 G6 | (C) riff 1   ‖ *To fade*

Hound Dog

Words & Music by
Jerry Leiber & Mike Stoller

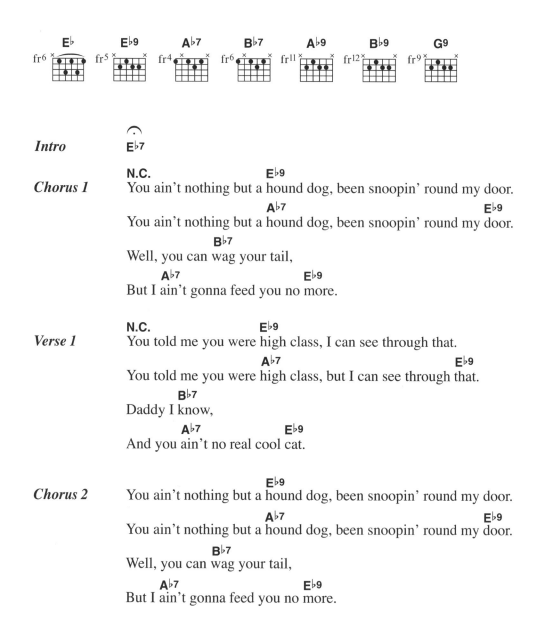

Intro   E♭7

Chorus 1
       N.C.   E♭9
You ain't nothing but a hound dog, been snoopin' round my door.
               A♭7   E♭9
You ain't nothing but a hound dog, been snoopin' round my door.
        B♭7
Well, you can wag your tail,
     A♭7   E♭9
But I ain't gonna feed you no more.

Verse 1
       N.C.   E♭9
You told me you were high class, I can see through that.
                A♭7   E♭9
You told me you were high class, but I can see through that.
        B♭7
Daddy I know,
     A♭7   E♭9
And you ain't no real cool cat.

Chorus 2
                E♭9
You ain't nothing but a hound dog, been snoopin' round my door.
               A♭7   E♭9
You ain't nothing but a hound dog, been snoopin' round my door.
        B♭7
Well, you can wag your tail,
     A♭7   E♭9
But I ain't gonna feed you no more.

Solo	‖: E♭9	E♭9	E♭9	E♭9	A♭9	A♭9	
(w/vocal							
ad lib.)	E♭9	E♭9	B♭9	A♭9 G9	E♭9	B♭9 :‖

Verse 2

                E♭9
Baby feel so blue, you made me weep and moan.

        A♭7   **E♭9**
Baby feel so blue, honey you made me weep and moan.

                B♭7
Ain't lookin' for a woman,

       A♭7   **E♭9**
All you lookin' for is home.

Chorus 3   As Chorus 1

Ending   'And Bow-wow to you too, honey!'

How Long How Long Blues

Words & Music by
Leroy Carr & Ann Egberg

E   E7   A   A7   B7

Tune Guitar down a semitone

Intro

| E | E7 | A | A7 |

| E | B7 | E   B7 | E |

Verse 1

    E   E7
How long, baby how long,

       A7
Has that evening train been gone,

    E   B7   E B7 | E
How long, how, how long, baby how long.

Verse 2

   E   E7
I stood at the station, watched my baby leaving town,

       A7
Feeling dis - gusted, nowhere could peace be found,

   E   B7   E B7 | E
How long, how, how long, baby how long.

Verse 3

   E   E7
I can hear the whistle blowing but I cannot see no train,

       A7
And it's deep down in my heart baby, there lies an aching pain,

   E   B7   E B7 | E
How long, how, how long, baby how long.

Verse 4

       E   **E⁷**
Sometimes I feel so disgusted, and I feel so blue,

    A⁷
That I hardly know what in this world baby just to do,

 E   **B⁷**   **E** **B⁷** ❘ **E**   ‖
How long, how, how long, baby how long.

Verse 5

        E   **E⁷**
And if I could holler like I was a mountain train,

      A⁷
I'd go up on the mountain and I'd call my baby's name,

 E   **B⁷**   **E** **B⁷** ❘ **E**   ‖
How long, how, how long, baby how long.

Verse 6

       E   **E⁷**
And if someday you're gonna be sorry that you've done me wrong,

     A⁷
Well it will be too late, baby I will be gone,

 E   **B⁷**   **E** **B⁷** ❘ **E**   ‖
For so long, so long, baby so long.

Verse 7

      E   **E⁷**
My mind get's a-rambling, I feel so bad,

      A⁷
Thinking about the bad love, that I have had,

 E   **B⁷**   **E** **B⁷** ❘ **E**   ‖
How long, how, how long, baby how long.

I Ain't Superstitious

Words & Music by
Willie Dixon

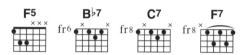

Tune Guitar Slightly Sharp

Intro

riff 1_____

| F A♭ B♭ A♭
3fr 1fr 3fr 1fr
④ ③ ③ ③ **F5 N.C.** | **riff 1** | **riff 1** ‖

Verse 1

(B♭7)
riff 2_____

B♭ B♭ A♭ B♭ A♭ F
6fr 8fr 6fr 8fr 6fr 8fr
⑥ ④ ④ ④ ④ ⑤ **w/riff 2**   **F5 N.C.** | **F5 N.C.** |
I ain't superstitious, (but) a black cat crossed my trail.

(B♭7)**w/riff 2** *(x2)*   **F5 N.C.** | **F5 N.C.** |
I ain't superstitious, but a black cat crossed my trail.

riff 3_____
(C7)

C   C   B♭ C   B♭ G
8fr 10fr 8fr 10fr 8fr 10fr
⑥ ④   ④   ④   ④   ⑤   **(B♭7)w/riff 2**   **F5 N.C.** | **F5 N.C.** ‖
Bad luck ain't got me so far, and I won't let it stop me now.

Verse 2

(B♭7)**w/riff 2**(x2)   **F5   N.C.**
The dogs begin to bark, all over my neighbour - hood.

                    F5   N.C. |
And that ain't all.

(B♭7)**w/riff 2**(x2)   **F5 N.C.** | **F5 N.C.** |
The dogs begin to bark, all over my neighbour - hood.

        (C7)**w/riff 2**   (B♭7)**w/riff 2**
This is a mean old world to live in, and I can't face it all by

        F5   N.C. | **F5 N.C.** ‖
my - self.

Link 1
w/straight crotchet triplet feel

‖: *(B♭7) | (B♭7) | F5 N.C. | F5 N.C. :‖

suggested harmony

| *(C7) | (B♭7) | F5 N.C. | F5 N.C. |

Verse 3

(B♭7)w/riff 2*(x2)* F5 N.C. | F5 N.C. |
Dogs begin to bark, all over my neighbour - hood.

(B♭7)w/riff 2*(x2)* F5 N.C. | F5 N.C. |
The dogs begin to bark, all over my neighbour - hood.

(C7)w/riff 3 (B♭7)w/riff 2
I got feeling about the future and it ain't too good,

F5 N.C. | F5 N.C. ‖
I know that.

Link 2
(w/vocal ad. lib.)

As Link 1

Verse 4

(B♭7)w/riff 2*(x2)*
Ain't superstitious, but a black cat crossed my trail,

F5 N.C. F5 N.C.
I said so one time before.

(B♭7)w/riff 2*(x2)* F5 N.C. | F5 N.C. |
Ain't superstitious, a black cat crossed my trail.

(C7)w/riff 3
Bad luck ain't got me so far, and you

(B♭7)w/riff 2 F5 N.C. | F5 N.C. ‖
Know I ain't gonna let it stop me now.

Solo

‖: F7 | F7 | F7 | F7 :‖ *Play 10 times*

‖: Drums | Drums | Drums | Drums :‖ *Play 3 times*

| F7 ‖

I Can't Quit You Baby

Words & Music by
Willie Dixon

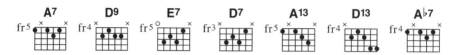

Tune guitar slightly flat

Verse 1

            A7   **D9**
Well, I can't quit you baby,

                              | **A7** | **A7** |
But I've got to put you down for a while.   Well,

     D9
You know, I can't quit you baby,

                              | **A7** | **A7** |
But I've got to put you down for a while.   Well,

       E7
You messed up my happy home baby,

D9 | **A7 D7** | **A7 E7** ‖
   Made me mistreat my only child.

Verse 2

             A7   **A13 A7**   **D9**
Yes you know I love you ba - by,

               D13 D9 | **A7 A13 A7** | **A13 A7** |
My love for you I'll never hide.   Oh,

     D9   **D13 D9 D13 D9**
You know I love you ba - by,

                        | **A7 A13 A7** | **A13 A7** |
My love for you I'll never hide.   Yes,

       E7   **D9**
You know I love you baby,

D9 | **A7 D7** | **A7 E7** ‖
Well you just my heart's desire.

Verse 3

A7   **D9**
Well, I'm so tired I could cry,
                              | **A7** | **A7** |
I could just lay down and   die.   Oh,

  D9
I'm so tired I could cry, ooh,
                              | **A7** | **A7** |
I could just lay down and   die.   Yes,

    E7
You know you're the only one darling,
D9 | **A7** **D7** | **A7** **E7** ‖
  Ooh, you know you're my desire.

                              A7
Verse 4   When you hear me moaning and groaning, baby,
D9 | **A7** **A13** **A7** | **A13** **A♭7** **A7** |
You know it hurts me way down inside.   Oh,
D9
When you hear me moaning and groaning, baby, oh,
                              | **A7** | **A7** |
You know it hurts me way down inside.   Oh,
E7
When you hear me holler, baby,
D9 | **A7** **D7** | **A7** **E7** ‖ *To fade*
Ooh you know you are my desire.

I'd Rather Go Blind

Words & Music by
Ellington Jordan & Billy Foster

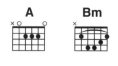

Intro　　| A 　| Bm 　| Bm 　| A 　‖

Verse 1

　　　　　　A　　　　　　　　　　　　Bm
　　　Something told me it was o - ver, (yeah),

　　　　　　　　　　　　　A
When I saw you and her talking.

　　　　　　　　　　　　　　　　　　Bm
Something deep down in my soul said "cry girl,"

　　　　　　　　　　　　　　　　　A
When I saw you and that girl　walking out.

Chorus 1

　　　　　　A
Ooh, I would rather,

　　　　　　　　　Bm
I would rather go blind, boy

Than to see you

　　　　　　　　　　　　　A
Walk away from me, child, no.

Ooh, so you see I love you so much,
Bm
　　But I don't want

To watch you leave me, babe.

Most of all, I just don't,
　　　　　　　A
I just don't want to be free, no.

Verse 2	**A** **Bm**
	Ooh, ooh, I was just, I was just,

Verse 2

        A   **Bm**
Ooh, ooh, I was just, I was just,

I was just sitting here thinking

                                     A
Of your kiss and your warm embrace, yeah.

When the reflection in the glass

               Bm
That I held to my lips now, babe (yeah, yeah),

Revealed the tears

                   A
That was on my face, yeah, ooh.

Chorus 2

 A
    And baby, baby I'd rather ,

               Bm
I'd rather be blind, boy,

Than to see you walk away,

                        A
See you walk away from me, yeah, ooh.

                                Bm
Baby, baby, baby, I'd rather be blind now.

Fade out

I'm A King Bee

Words & Music by
James Moore

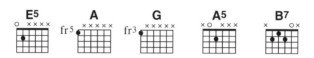

Capo first fret

Verse 1

riff 1 ⌐‾‾‾‾‾‾⌐
E5   A G E5 G (E5)   **riff 1** *(x2)*
Well I'm a king bee, buzz - ing around your hive.
                A5   **riff 1** *(x2)*
Well I'm a king bee, buzzing around your hive.
        B7   A5   **riff 1** *(x2)*
Well I can make honey baby, let me come in - side.

Verse 2

riff 1 *(x4)*
I'm young and able to buzz all night long.
            A5   **riff 1** *(x2)*
I'm young and able to buzz all night long.
        B7   A5   **riff 1** *(x2)*
Well when you hear me buzzin' baby, some stinging is going on.

Link 1

(E5)
| **riff 1** | **riff 1** | **riff 1** | **riff 1** | **riff 1** | **riff 1** |
  Well,   buzz a while.

| **riff 1** | **riff 1** | **riff 1** | **riff 1** | **riff 1** | **riff 1** | **riff 1** ‖
  Sting it then.

Verse 3

riff 1 *(x4)*
Well I'm a king bee, want you to be my queen.

 A5   **riff 1** *(x2)*
Well I'm a king bee, want you to be my queen.

                                       B7   **A5**   **riff 1** *(x2)*
Together we can make honey, the world ever never seen.

Instr

| riff 1 | riff 1 | riff 1 | riff 1 | |
| E5 A5 | A5 | riff 1 | riff 1 | |
| E5 B7 | A5 | riff 1 | riff 1 | ‖

Verse 4

riff 1 *(x4)*
Well I'm a king bee, can buzz all night long.

 A5   **riff 1** *(x2)*
Well I'm a king bee, can buzz all night long.

             B7   **A5**   **riff 1** *(x2)*
Well I can buzz better baby, when your man is gone.

Outro

 (E5)
‖: riff 1   :‖   *Repeat to fade*

101

I'm In The Mood

Words & Music by
John Lee Hooker & Bernard Besman

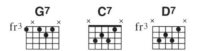

Intro | N.C. | N.C. | G⁷ | G⁷   ‖

Verse 1

G⁷
I'm in the mood,

I'm in the mood for love.

(C⁷)
I'm in the mood, I'm in the mood,

                G⁷
Baby, I'm in the mood for love.

I said night time is the right time,

     (C⁷)
To be with the one you love.

You know when night come baby,

God know, you're so far away.

     (C⁷)
I'm in the mood, I'm in the mood,

             G⁷
I'm in the mood for love.

     D⁷
I'm in the mood, in the mood,

    (C⁷)
Baby,   in the mood for love.

Link		G⁷		G⁷		G⁷		G⁷		
		C⁷		C⁷		G⁷		G⁷		

Verse 2

       G⁷
I said hey yes, my mother told me,

To leave that girl alone,

But my mother didn't know what that little girl was puttin' down.

      (C⁷)
I'm in the mood,

I'm in the mood,

      G⁷
Baby, in the mood for love.

      (D⁷)
I'm in the mood,

      (C⁷)
I'm in the mood,

             G⁷ | G⁷ ‖
Baby, in the mood for love.

(I'm Your) Hoochie Coochie Man

Words & Music by
Willie Dixon

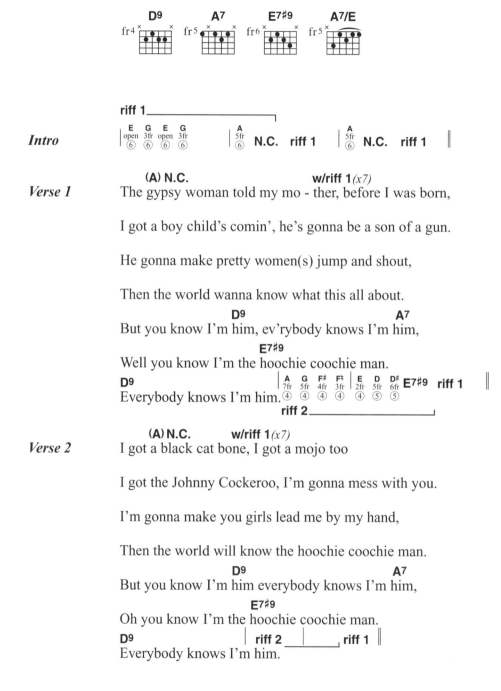

Intro

Verse 1

(A) N.C.   w/riff **1** *(x7)*
The gypsy woman told my mo - ther, before I was born,

I got a boy child's comin', he's gonna be a son of a gun.

He gonna make pretty women(s) jump and shout,

Then the world wanna know what this all about.
                          D9   **A7**
But you know I'm him, ev'rybody knows I'm him,
                 E7♯9
Well you know I'm the hoochie coochie man.
D9
Everybody knows I'm him.

Verse 2

(A) N.C.   w/riff **1** *(x7)*
I got a black cat bone, I got a mojo too

I got the Johnny Cockeroo, I'm gonna mess with you.

I'm gonna make you girls lead me by my hand,

Then the world will know the hoochie coochie man.
                          D9   **A7**
But you know I'm him everybody knows I'm him,
                 E7♯9
Oh you know I'm the hoochie coochie man.
D9
Everybody knows I'm him.

Verse 3

(A) N.C.   **w/riff 1** *(x7)*

On the seventh hours, on the seventh day,

On the seventh month, the seven doctors say.

He was born for good luck and that you'll see,

I got seven hundred dollars don't you mess with me.

D9   **A7**

But you know I'm him, ev'rybody knows I'm him,

               E7♯9

Well you know I'm the hoochie coochie man.

D9   A G F♯ F E D D♯ **A7/E**

Ev'rybody knows I'm him.   7fr 5fr 4fr 3fr 2fr 5fr 6fr

                                ④ ④ ④ ④ ④ ⑤ ⑤

Key To The Highway

Words & Music by
Big Bill Broonzy & Charles Segar

Intro
| D7* | C7 | G7* C7 | G7 D7 |
| G7 | G | C7 | C7 |
| G7 | D7 | G7 C7 | G7 D7 ‖

Verse 1

         G7   D7   G7
I got   the key to the highway, and I'm billled out and bound to go.

                 D7
I'm gonna leave here runnin',

C7   G7   C7 | G7   D7 ‖
'Cause walking is most too slow.

Verse 2

             G7   D7   G7
I'm going down on the bor - der, now where I'm better known.

                 D7
'Cause woman, you don't do nothin',

C7   G7   C7 | G7   D7 ‖
But drive a good man away from home.

Verse 3

                G7   D7   G7
Now when the moon creeps over the moun - tain, I'll be on my way.

                 D7
Now, and I'm gonna walk this old highway,

C7   G7   C7 | G7   D7 ‖
Until the break o' day.

Instr.
‖: G7 | C7 | C7 |
| G7 | D7 | G7 C7 | G7 D7 :‖

© Copyright 1941 & 1963 Leeds Music Corporation, USA.
Universal/MCA Music Limited.
All rights in Germany administered by Universal/MCA Music Publ. GmbH.
All Rights Reserved. International Copyright Secured.

Verse 4

      G⁷   **D⁷**   **G⁷**
Run   here, sweet ma - ma, now, and help me with this heavy load,

          D⁷
I am due in west Texas,

        C⁷   **G⁷**   **C⁷** | **G⁷**   **D⁷** ‖
And I've got to get on the road.

Verse 5

      G⁷   **D⁷**   **G⁷**
I'm goin' to west Texas, I'm goin' down behind the sun,

          D⁷
I'm goin'   to ask the good Lord,

      C⁷   **G⁷**   **C⁷** | **G⁷**   **D⁷** ‖
What evil I have done?

Outro

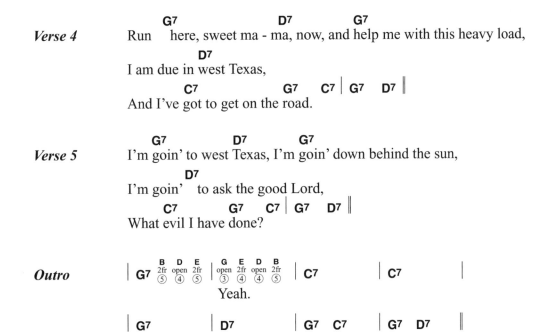

| **G⁷** B D E | G E D B | **C⁷** | **C⁷** | |
Yeah.

| **G⁷** | **D⁷** | **G⁷** **C⁷** | **G⁷** **D⁷** ‖

Killing Floor

Words & Music by
Chester Burnette

E7/D   D7/C   A7   E7   A/E

Bm(no5)   A/C#   D/A   Em(no5)   D/F#

Intro | E7/D | D7/C | A7 | E7 ‖

riff 1_____

Link 1 | A/E Bm(no5) | A/C# | A/E Bm(no5) | A/C# |

         | D/A Em(no5) | D/F# | A/E Bm(no5) | A/C# |

         | E7/D | D7/C | A7 | E7 ‖

w/riff 1
Verse 1 I should have quit you, a long time ago.

I should have quit you, baby, 'long time ago.
                E7/D   D7/C   **A7** | **E7** ‖
I should have quit you, and went on to Mexico.

w/riff 1
Verse 2 If I had a - followed, my first mind.

If I had a - followed, my first mind.
              E7/D   D7/C   **A7** | **E7** ‖
I'd a-been gone, since my second time.

Link 2 As Link 1

w/riff 1

Verse 3   I should have went on, when my friend come from Mexico at me.

I should have went on, when my friend come from Mexico at me.

E⁷/D   **D⁷/C**
But no, I was foolin' with you baby,

A⁷ ‖ **E⁷**   ‖
I let you put me on the killin' floor.

w/riff 1

Verse 4   Lord knows, I should have been gone.

Lord knows, I should have been gone.

E⁷/D   **D⁷/C**
And I wouldn't have been here,

A⁷ ‖ **E⁷**   ‖
Down on the killin' floor.

Outro   As Link 1. *To fade.*

La Grange

Words & Music by
Billy Gibbons, Dusty Hill & Frank Beard

A5   **G/A**   **Am**   **C**   **D**

C5   **E♭5**   **F5**   **C5(6)**   **Fm(no5)**   **F(no5)**

Intro | A5 | A5   G/A Am | Am   A5 | A5   G/A Am |

| Am   A5   ‖

riff 1 ⎯⎯⎯⎯⎯⎯⎯ **(A5)**

                 G/A   **A5**   **C**   **D** w/riff 1 *(x8)*

Verse 1   Rumour   spread - in' around in that   Tex - as town,

         C   D   A
About that shack outside La Grange.

     C   C   D   A   C D   D
And you know what I'm talkin' about,

A   C D   A
Just let me know if you wanna go.

      C   D   A
To that home out on the range,

C   D A   C   D
They gotta lotta nice girls, oh.

         A5
         w/riff 1 *(x4)*
Bridge   Have mercy,

A   C   D
A haw, haw, haw, haw.

A
A haw, a haw, haw, haw.

A5

w/riff 1 *(x8)*   *C   D   A*

Verse 2   Well, I hear it's fine if you've got the time,

C   D   A   *C   D   A*
And that ten to get yourself in ahmm, hmm,

C   D   A   *C   D   A*
And I hear it's tight most every night,

C D   A   *C D   A   C D*
But now I might be mistaken.

Play 8 times

Instr   ‖: **C5** | **C5 E♭5 F5** | **C5** | **C5 E♭5 F5**   :‖

‖: **C5(6)** | **Fm(no5)** | **F(no5)** | **A5** C C# **A5** :‖
                                                          3fr 4fr
                                                          ⑤   ⑤

Breakdown | **A5** | **A5 G/A Am** | **Am   A5** | **A5   G/A Am** |

| **Am   A5** | **A5 G/A Am** | **Am   A5** | **N.C.**   ‖

Outro   ‖: **A5** | **A5 C D** :‖ *Repeat to fade*

111

Love In Vain

Words & Music by
Robert Johnson

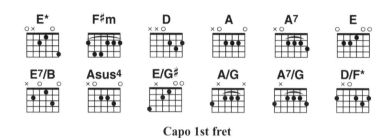

Capo 1st fret

Intro | E* | F#m D | D A A7 | E ‖

Well I...

Verse 1

A   A7
Followed her to the station   with a suitcase in my hand,

D   E7/B
Yeah, I followed her to the sta - tion,

                   A   E | Asus4 A |
With a suitcase in my hand.

            E   E/G#
Well, it's hard to tell, it's hard to tell,

F#m   D   A A7 | E ‖
  When all your love's in vain.   When the

Verse 2

A   A7
Train come in the sta - tion,   I looked her in the eye,

           D   E7/B
Well, the train come in the sta - tion,

                A   E | Asus4 A |
I looked her in the eye.

         E   F#m
Well, I felt so sad so lonesome,

             D   A A7 | E ‖
That I could not help but cry.

Instr.

| A   A/G | A   A/G | A   A/G | A⁷   A⁷/G |
| D   D/F♯ | E⁷/B | A   E | Asus⁴   A |
| E | F♯m   D | A   A⁷ | E ‖

When the

Verse 2

A   A/G   A A/G A⁷ A⁷/G
Train   left the sta - tion,   it had   two lights on behind,

          D   D/F♯
Yeah, when the train had left the station,

  E⁷/B   A E | Asus⁴ A |
It had two lights on be - hind.

       E   F♯m
Well, the blue light was my baby,

          D   A A⁷ | E ‖
And the red light was my mind.

Outro

| A   A/G | A   A/G | A   A/G | A⁷   A⁷/G |
  All   my   love's   in   vain.

| D   D/F♯ | E⁷/B | A   E | Asus⁴   A |

| E   E/G♯ | F♯m   D | A   A⁷ | E   A⁷ ‖
    All my love's in vain.

Meet Me In The Morning

Words & Music by
Bob Dylan

A   **E**   **A7**   **B7**

Tune guitar slightly sharp

riff 1 ⎯⎯⎯⎯

G E D E
3fr open 3fr open
① ① ② ①

Intro | A | E   A | riff 1 |

| riff 1 | riff 1   A | E   ‖

Verse 1

E
Meet me in the morning,
A7 | riff 1*ad lib.*   A | riff 1*ad lib.* |
  56th and Waba - sha,

A7
Meet me in the morning,
      | riff 1*ad lib.*   A | riff 1*ad lib.* |
56th and Waba - sha,   Honey,

B7
We could be in Kansas,
A7 | riff 1*ad lib.*   A | riff 1*ad lib.* |
By time the snow begins to thaw.

Verse 2

E
They say the darkest hour,
A7 | riff 1*ad lib.*   A | riff 1*ad lib.* |
  Is right before the dawn.

A7
They say the darkest hour,
      | riff 1*ad lib.*   A | riff 1*ad lib.* |
Is right before the dawn.   Honey,

B7
You wouldn't know it by me,
A7 | riff 1*ad lib.*   A | riff 1*ad lib.* |
Every day's been darkness since you been gone.

Verse 3

E
Little rooster crowin',

A⁷ | **riff 1***ad lib.* **A** | **riff 1***ad lib.* |
   There must be something on his mind,

A⁷
Little rooster crowin',

| **riff 1***ad lib.* **A** | **riff 1***ad lib.* |
There must be something on his mind,

B⁷
Well, I feel just like that rooster

A⁷ | **riff 1***ad lib.* **A** | **riff 1***ad lib.* |
Honey, ya treat me so un - kind.   Well, I

Verse 4

E
Struggled through barbed wire,

A⁷ | **riff 1***ad lib.* **A** | **riff 1***ad lib.* |
   Felt the hail fall from a - bove.

     A⁷
Well, I struggled through barbed wire,

| **riff 1***ad lib.* **A** | **riff 1***ad lib.* |
Felt the hail fall from a - bove.

     B⁷
Well, you know I even outrun the hound dogs,

A⁷ | **riff 1***ad lib.* **A** | **riff 1***ad lib.* |
Honey, I know I've earned your love.

Verse 5

E
Look at the sun,

A⁷ | **riff 1***ad lib.* **A** | **riff 1***ad lib.* |
   Sinkin' like a ship.

A⁷ | **riff 1***ad lib.* **A** | **riff 1***ad lib.* |
Look at the sun, sinkin' like a ship.

   B⁷
Ain't that just like my heart, babe,

A⁷ | **riff 1***ad lib.* **A** | **riff 1***ad lib.* |
When you kissed my lips?

Outro

‖: E | A⁷ | **riff 1** **A** | **riff 1** |

| A⁷ | A⁷ | **riff 1** **A** | **riff 1** |

| B⁷ | A⁷ | **riff 1** **A** | **riff 1** :‖ *Repeat to fade*

115

My Babe

Words & Music by
Willie Dixon

F   B♭   C   F/A   F7   B♭7   C7

riff 1 _____

Intro

| F F B♭ B♭ | F |

| F F B♭ B♭ | F |

| F F B♭ B♭ | F ‖

w/riff 1 *(x3)*

Verse 1

My baby don't stand no cheatin', my babe.

riff 2 _____

C C F/A F/A | C |

Oh yeah she don't stand no cheatin', my babe.

    F   **F7**

Oh yeah she don't stand no cheatin',

    B♭7 N.C.

She   don't stand none of that midnight creepin',

    w/riff 1 *(x2)*

My babe, true little baby, my babe.

    w/riff 1 *(x3)*

Verse 2

My babe, I know she love me, my babe.

       w/riff 2 *(x1)*

Oh yes, I know she love me, my babe.

    F   **F7**

Oh yes, I know she love me,

    B♭7 N.C.

She   don't do nothin' but kiss and hug me,

    w/riff 1 *(x2)*

My babe, true little baby, my babe.

Instr

F	F	F	F7
B♭7	B♭7	F	F
C7	C7	F	F

Verse 3

w/riff 1 *(x3)*
My baby don't stand no cheatin', my babe.

        w/riff 2 *(x1)*
Oh no, she don't stand no cheatin', my babe.

   F   F7
Oh no, she don't stand no cheatin',

   B♭7 N.C.
Ev' - rything she do she do so pleasin',

  w/riff 1 *(x2)*
My babe, true little baby, my babe.

Verse 4

  w/riff 1 *(x3)*
My baby don't stand no foolin', my babe.

       w/riff 2 *(x1)*
Oh yeah, she don't stand no foolin', my babe.

  F   F7
Oh yeah, she don't stand no foolin',

B♭7 N.C.
When she's hot there ain't no coolin'.

Outro

w/riff 1
My babe, true little baby, my babe,

‖: She's my baby (true little baby). :‖ *Repeat to fade*

Need Your Love So Bad

Words & Music by
Mertis John Jr.

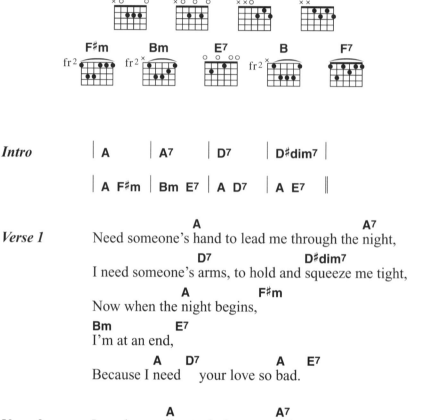

Intro

| A | A⁷ | D⁷ | D♯dim⁷ |

| A F♯m | Bm E⁷ | A D⁷ | A E⁷ ‖

Verse 1

             A   A⁷
Need someone's hand to lead me through the night,
              D⁷   D♯dim⁷
I need someone's arms, to hold and squeeze me tight,
             A   F♯m
Now when the night begins,
Bm   E⁷
I'm at an end,
         A   D⁷   A   E⁷
Because I need   your love so bad.

Verse 2

           A   A⁷
I need some lips to feel next to mine,
            D⁷   D♯dim⁷
I need someone to stand up and tell me when I'm lying,
         A   F♯m   Bm   E⁷
And when the lights are low   and it's time to go,
         A   D⁷   A   A⁷
That's when I need   your love so bad.

Bridge

                   D⁷
So why don't you give it up,

         D♯dim⁷
And bring it home to me,

              A
Or write it on a piece of paper baby

        A⁷
So it can be read to me.

              B
Tell me that you love me

And stop driving me mad,

       E⁷ F⁷   **E⁷**
Oh because I,   I need your love so bad.

Verse 3

             A   **A⁷**
Need your soft voice to talk to me at night,

                D⁷
I don't want you to worry baby,

                D♯dim⁷
I know we can make everything alright.

A   **F♯m Bm**   **E⁷**
Listen to my plea baby,   bring it to me,

         A   **D⁷**   **A**   **E⁷**
Because I need   your love so bad.

Outro

‖: A | A⁷ | D⁷ | D♯dim⁷ |

| A F♯m | Bm E⁷ | A D⁷ | A E⁷ :‖ *Repeat to fade*

Old Love

Words & Music by
Eric Clapton & Robert Cray

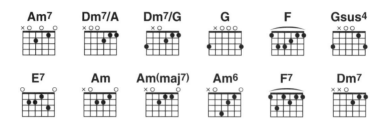

(2 bar count in)

Intro ‖: Am⁷ Dm⁷/A │ Dm⁷/G G │ Am⁷ Dm⁷/A │ Dm⁷/G G :‖

Verse 1

Am⁷   Dm⁷/A   Dm⁷/G G
I can feel your body

Am⁷ F   Gsus⁴ G
When I'm lyin' in my bed,

Am⁷   Dm⁷/A Dm⁷/G G
Too much confusion

Am⁷ F   Gsus⁴   G
Goin' round through my head.

F   E⁷
And it's makin' me so angry,

             Am   Am(maj⁷) Am⁷ Am⁶
To know that the flame still burns.

F
Why can't I get over

E⁷   F⁷   E⁷ N.C.
And when will I ever learn?

Chorus 1

     Am⁷ Dm⁷ Dm⁷/G G
Old love,

        Am⁷ Dm⁷ Dm⁷/G G
Leave me alone.

Am⁷   Dm⁷ Dm⁷/G G
Old love,

Am⁷   Dm⁷ Dm⁷/G G
Go on home.

Verse 2

Am⁷   Dm⁷/A   Dm⁷/G   G
I can see your face

Am⁷   F   Gsus⁴ G
But I know it's not real.

Am⁷ Dm⁷/A   Dm⁷/G   G
Just an illusion

Am⁷   F   Gsus⁴ G
Caused by how I used to feel. ___

F   E⁷
Makes me so angry

                     Am   Am(maj⁷) Am⁷ Am⁶
To know that the flame will always burn.

F   E⁷
Never get over,

                        F⁷   E⁷   N.C.
Know now that I'll never learn, never learn.

Chorus 2   As Chorus 1

Solo

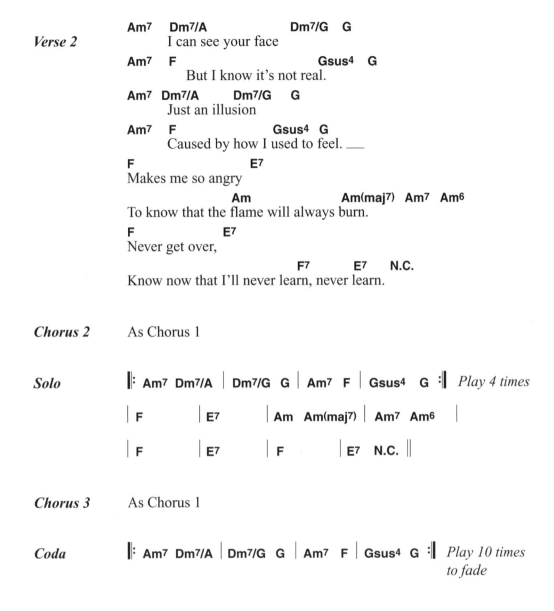

‖: Am⁷ Dm⁷/A | Dm⁷/G G | Am⁷ F | Gsus⁴ G :‖ *Play 4 times*

| F | E⁷ | Am Am(maj⁷) | Am⁷ Am⁶ |

| F | E⁷ | F   · | E⁷ N.C. ‖

Chorus 3   As Chorus 1

Coda

‖: Am⁷ Dm⁷/A | Dm⁷/G G | Am⁷ F | Gsus⁴ G :‖ *Play 10 times*
                                                     to fade

On The Road Again

Words & Music by
Allen Wilson & Floyd Jones

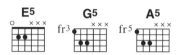

Fade in

Intro

| (Em) | (Em) | (Em) | (Em) | (Em) |

| E5 | E5 | E5 G5 A5 | E5 |

Well I'm...

Verse 1

(E5)
So tired of crying, but I'm out on the road again,
    G5 A5 E5
I'm on the road again.

(E5)
Well, I'm so tired of crying, but I'm out on the road again,
    G5 A5 E5
I'm on the road again.

   (E5)   G5 A5 E5
I ain't got no woman just to call my special friend.

   (E5)
You know the first time I travelled out in the rain and snow,
G5 A5 E5
In the rain and snow.

   (E5)
You know the first time I travelled out in the rain and snow,
G5 A5 E5
In the rain and snow.

   (E5)   G5 A5 E5
I didn't have no payroll, not even no place to go.

   (E5)
And my dear mother left me when I was quite young,
G5 A5 E5
When I was quite young.

   (E5)
And my dear mother left me when I was quite young,
G5 A5 E5
When I was quite young.

    (E5)   G5 A5 E5
She said "Lord, have mercy on my wicked son."

Instr. 𝄆 (E5) | (E5) | E5 G5 A5 | (E5) 𝄇

| E5 | E5 | E5 G5 A5 | E5 𝄀

Take a...

Verse 2

(E5)
Hint from me, mama, please don't you cry no more,

    G5 A5 E5
Don't you cry no more.

    (E5)   G5 A5 E5
Take a hint from me, mama, please don't you cry no more,

    G5 A5 E5
Don't you cry no more.

    (E5)   G5 A5 E5
'Cause it's soon one morning down the road I'm going.

    (E5)
But I ain't going down that long old lonesome road,

  G5 A5   E5
All by myself.

    (E5)
But I ain't going down that long old lonesome road,

  G5 A5   E5
All by myself.

    (E5)   G5 A5 E5
I can't carry you baby, gonna carry somebody else.

Outro 𝄆 E5 | E5 | E5 G5 A5 | E5 𝄇

Repeat to fade

123

One Bourbon, One Scotch, One Beer

Words & Music by
John Lee Hooker

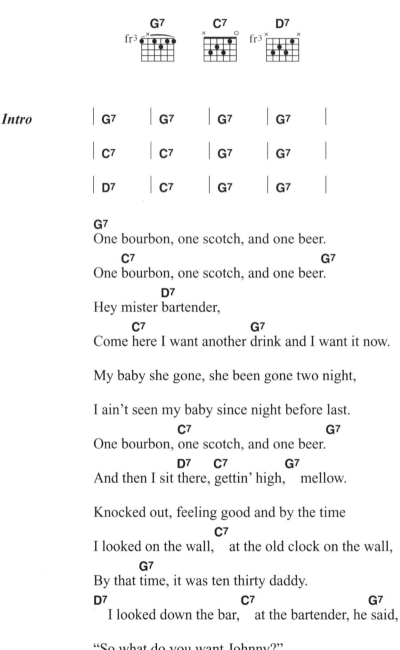

Intro

| G⁷ | G⁷ | G⁷ | G⁷ |

| C⁷ | C⁷ | G⁷ | G⁷ |

| D⁷ | C⁷ | G⁷ | G⁷ |

G⁷
One bourbon, one scotch, and one beer.
   C⁷   **G⁷**
One bourbon, one scotch, and one beer.
          D⁷
Hey mister bartender,
       C⁷   **G⁷**
Come here I want another drink and I want it now.

My baby she gone, she been gone two night,

I ain't seen my baby since night before last.
          C⁷   **G⁷**
One bourbon, one scotch, and one beer.
          D⁷ **C⁷**   **G⁷**
And then I sit there, gettin' high,   mellow.

Knocked out, feeling good and by the time
               C⁷
I looked on the wall,   at the old clock on the wall,
      G⁷
By that time, it was ten thirty daddy.
D⁷   **C⁷**   **G⁷**
  I looked down the bar,   at the bartender, he said,

"So what do you want Johnny?"

                                              C7
One bourbon, one scotch, and one beer.
                                    G7
Well, my baby she gone, she been gone two night,
                          D7
I ain't seen my baby since night before last,
         C7   **G7**
I wan - na get drunk till I'm off of my mind,

One bourbon, one scotch, and one beer.
                  C7
And I sat there,   gettin' high,
G7   **D7**
Stoned, knocked out, and   by the time
C7   **G7**
I looked on the wall, at the old clock again,

And by that time, It was a quarter to two,
               C7
Last call for alcohol, I said,
                        G7   **D7**
'Hey mister barten - der', he said, 'What do you want?'
       C7   **G7**
One bourbon, one scotch, and one   beer.

One bourbon, one scotch, and one beer.
C7   **G7**
One bourbon, one scotch, and one beer. *To fade*

Parisienne Walkways

Words & Music by
Gary Moore & Phil Lynott

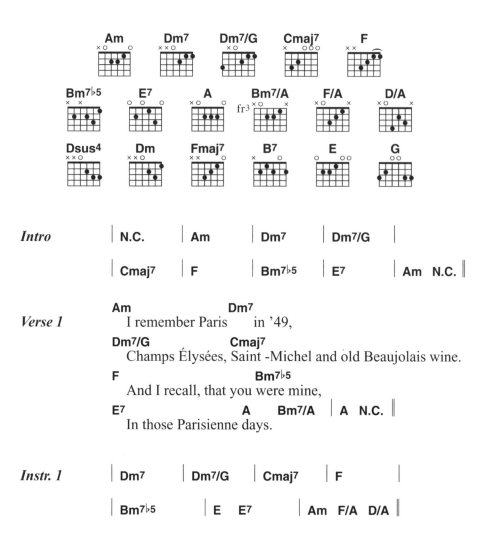

Intro	| N.C.	| Am	| Dm7	| Dm7/G	|
	| Cmaj7	| F	| Bm7♭5	| E7	| Am N.C. ‖

Verse 1

    Am   Dm7
I remember Paris   in '49,

   Dm7/G   Cmaj7
Champs Élysées, Saint -Michel and old Beaujolais wine.

   F   Bm7♭5
And I recall, that you were mine,

   E7   A   Bm7/A | A N.C. ‖
In those Parisienne days.

Instr. 1	| Dm7	| Dm7/G	| Cmaj7	| F	|
	| Bm7♭5		| E E7	| Am F/A D/A ‖	

Verse 2

N.C.   **Dsus4**   **Dm**
Looking back at the photographs,

Dm7/G   **Cmaj7**
 Those summer days spend outside corner cafés

Fmaj7   **Bm7♭5**
 Oh, I could write you paragraphs,

      B7   **E**   **F** | **E** **N.C.** | **N.C.**   ‖
A - bout my old Parisienne days.

Instr. 2 | **Dm** | **Dm7/G** | **Cmaj7** | **Fmaj7** |

                | **Bm7♭5** **E** | **Am** **Dm** | **Am** **F** **E** | **Am** **Dm** |

                | **Am** **F** **E** | **Am** **Dm** | **Am** **F** **E** | **Am** **Dm** |

                | **Am** **F** **E** | **Am** **Dm** | **Am**   ‖ *To fade*

Presence Of The Lord

Words & Music by
Eric Clapton

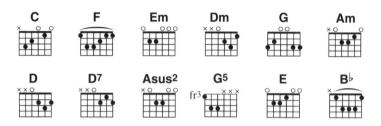

Intro
| C F Em Dm | C F Em Dm | C F Em Dm | C F Em Dm ‖

Verse 1

C G   Am
I have finally found a way to live,

F   C F Em Dm
Just like I never could before.

C G   Am   D
I know that I don't have   much to give

                      G   N.C. Em G
But I can open any door.

Chorus 1

Am   F   N.C. Em G
Everybody knows the secret,

Am   D7   G
Oh, everybody knows the score, yeah, yeah, yeah, yeah.

C   G   Am
I have finally found a way to live

F   G   (C)
In the colour of the Lord.

Link 1
| C F Em Dm | C F Em Dm ‖
(Lord.)

Verse 2

C   G   Am
I have finally found a place to live

F   C F Em Dm
Just like I never could before.

C   G   Am   D
And I know I don't have   much to give

                      G   N.C. Em G
But soon I'll open any door.

Chorus 2

Am   F   N.C. Em G
Everybody knows the secret,

Am   D7   G
Oh, everybody knows the score, _____

C   G   Am
I have finally found a place to live

F   G   C   F Em Dm C
In the presence of the Lord,

F   Em   Dm   Asus2
In the presence of the Lord.

Link 2
(Double time)

| N.C. | N.C. | N.C. | N.C. ‖

Instrumental

‖: Am | Am | Am | Am :‖

| D7 | D7 | D7 | D7 |

| E | E | E | E |

| G5 | C | B♭ | G ‖

Link 3
(Half time)

| C F Em Dm | C F Em Dm ‖

Verse 3

C   G   Am
I have finally found a way to live,

                        C F Em Dm
Just like I never could before.

C   G   Am   D
And I know I don't have much to give

                    G   N.C. Em G
But I can open any door.

Chorus 3

Am   F   N.C. Em G
Everybody knows the secret,

Am   D7   G
I said, 'cos everybody knows the score. _____

C   G   Am
I have finally found a way to live

F   G   C   F Em Dm C
In the colour of the Lord,

F   Em   Dm   C   F Em Dm | C |
In the colour of the Lord.

Pride And Joy

Words & Music by
Stevie Ray Vaughan

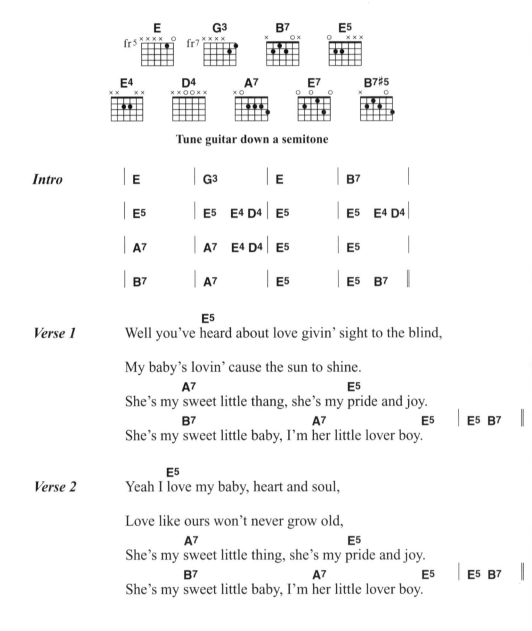

Tune guitar down a semitone

Intro | E | G♯3 | E | B7 |

| E5 | E5 E4 D4 | E5 | E5 E4 D4 |

| A7 | A7 E4 D4 | E5 | E5 |

| B7 | A7 | E5 | E5 B7 ||

Verse 1

E5
Well you've heard about love givin' sight to the blind,

My baby's lovin' cause the sun to shine.
    A7   E5
She's my sweet little thang, she's my pride and joy.
    B7   A7   E5 | E5 B7 ||
She's my sweet little baby, I'm her little lover boy.

Verse 2

E5
Yeah I love my baby, heart and soul,

Love like ours won't never grow old,
    A7   E5
She's my sweet little thing, she's my pride and joy.
    B7   A7   E5 | E5 B7 ||
She's my sweet little baby, I'm her little lover boy.

Verse 3

E5 N.C.   **E5 N.C.**
Yeah I love my lady, she's long and lean,

E5 N.C.   **E7**
You mess with her, you'll see a man get mean.

       A7   **E5**
She's my sweet little thing, she's my pride and joy.

       B7   **A7**   **E5** | **E5 B7** ‖
She's my sweet little baby, I'm her little lover boy.

Solo

‖: **E5** | **E5** | **E5** | **E7** |

| **A7** | **A7** | **E5** | **E5** |

| **B7** | **A7** | **E5** | **E5 B7** :‖

Verse 4

E5 N.C.   **E5 N.C.**
Well I love my baby, like the finest wine,

E5 N.C.
Stick with her until the end of time.

       A7   **E5**
She's my sweet little thing, she's my pride and joy.

       B7   **A7**   **E5** | **E5 B7** ‖
She's my sweet little baby, I'm her little lover boy.

Verse 5   As Verse 2

Outro

| **E5** | **E5** | **E5** | **E5** |

| **A7** | **A7** | **E5** | **E5** |

| **B7** | **A7** | **E5** | **E5 B7 B7♯5** |

| **E5**   ‖

Reconsider Baby

Words & Music by
Lowell Fulson

Intro

| G7 | C9 | G7 | G7 |
| C9 | C9 | G7 | G7 |
| D7 | C9 | G7 C9 | G7 D7 ‖

Verse 1

G7   C9   G7
So long, oh how I hate to see you go.
   C9   G7
So long, oh how I hate to see you go.
      D7   C9
And the way that I will miss you,
                    G7 | G7 ‖
I guess you will never know.

Verse 2

          G7   C9   G7
We've been together so long, to have to separate this way.
     C9   G7
We've been together so long, to have to separate this way.
             D7   C9
I'm gonna let you go ahead on baby,
                         G7 | G7 ‖
Pray that you'll come back home some day.

Instr ‖: As Intro :‖

Verse 3

           G7   **C9**
You said you once had loved me,

                                 G7
But now I guess you have changed your mind.

            C9
You said you once had loved me,

                                 G7
But now I guess you have changed your mind.

         D7   **C9**
Why don't you reconsider baby.

                        G7 | **G7** **A♭7** **G7** ‖
Give yourself just a little more time

Red House

Words & Music by
Jimi Hendrix

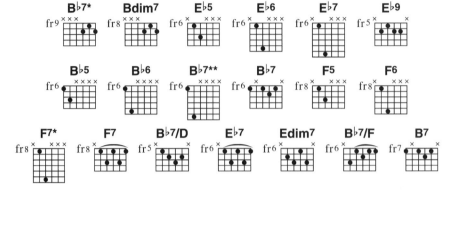

*chords reflect overall tonality

Intro

| *B♭7* | *B♭dim7 *B♭7 | N.C | N.C |
Oh yeah!

riff 2 _____   riff 1_____

| E♭5 E♭6 E♭7 E♭6 | (E♭9)w/riff 2 | B♭5 B♭6 B♭7** B♭6 | (B♭7)w/riff 1 |

riff 3 _____

| F5 F6 F7* F6 | (E♭9)w/riff 2 | (B♭7)w/riff 1 | B♭7 F7 ‖

Verse 1

    (B♭7)w/riff 1   (E♭9)w/riff 2   (B♭7)w/riff 1 *(x2)*
There's a red house   over yonder, that's where my baby stays.
(E♭9)w/riff 2 *(x2)*
Oh there's a red house over yonder,
          (B♭7)w/riff 1 *(x2)*
Lord that's where my baby stays.
(F7)w/riff 3
I ain't been home to see my baby,
(E♭9)w/riff 2   (B♭7)w/riff 1 | B♭7 F7 ‖
In ninety-nine and one half days.

Verse 2

(B♭7)**w/riff 1**
Wait minute something's wrong here,

(E♭9)**w/riff 2**   (B♭7)**w/riff 1** *(x2)*
The key won't unlock this door.

(E♭9)**w/riff 2** *(x2)*
Wait a minute something's wrong,

                             (B♭7)**w/riff 1** *(x2)*
Lord have mercy this key won't unlock this door.

Something's going wrong here.

       (F7)**w/riff 3**   (B♭7)**w/riff 1**   (B♭7)**w/riff 1** *(x2)*
I have a bad bad feeling, that my baby don't live here no more.

B♭7   **F7**
That's alright I still got my guitar, look out now.

Solo

| (B♭7)**w/riff 1** | (E♭9)**w/riff 2** | (B♭7)**w/riff 1** *(x2)* | **B♭7** | |

| (E♭9)**w/riff 2** *(x2)* | **E♭9** | (B♭7)**w/riff 1** *(x2)* | **B♭7** | |

| (F7)**w/riff 3** | (E♭9)**w/riff 2** | (B♭7)**w/riff 1** *(x2)* | **B♭7** **F7** ‖

Verse 3

                  (B♭7)**w/riff 1**   (E♭9)**w/riff 2**   (B♭7)**w/riff 1** *(x2)*
Well, I might as well a go back over yonder, way back upon the hill.

        (E♭9)**w/riff 2** *(x2)*
Lord I might as well go back over yonder,

                 (B♭7)**w/riff 1** *(x2)*
Way back yonder across the hill.

(F7)**w/riff 3**   **E♭9 N.C.**
'Cause if my baby don't love me no more,

           B♭7 **B♭7/D** **E♭7** **Edim7** | **B♭7/F** **B7** **B♭7** ‖
I know her sister will.

The Red Rooster

Words & Music by
Willie Dixon

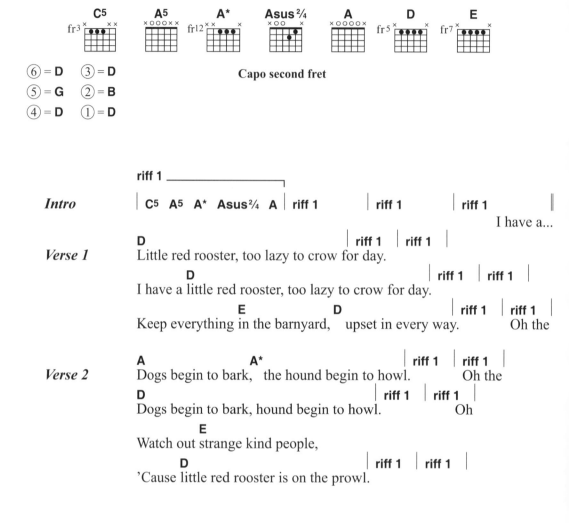

		riff 1	riff 1

A*

Verse 3   If you see   my little red rooster, please drag him home.   If you

D | riff 1 | riff 1 |

See my little red rooster, please drag him home.

                                        E

There ain't no peace   in the barnyard,

D | riff 1 | riff 1 |

Since the little red rooster been gone.

Outro | riff 1 | riff 1   ‖ *To fade*

Roadhouse Blues

Words & Music by
Jim Morrison, Robbie Krieger, Ray Manzarek & John Densmore

E7 A B C C# D D# E

Intro   ‖: E7 | E7 | E7 | E7 :‖   *play 3 times*

Verse 1
            E7
Keep your eyes on the road,

Your hands upon the wheel.

Keep your eyes on the road,

Your hands upon the wheel.

Yeah, we're going to the Roadhouse.

We're gonna have a real,

Good time.

| E7 | E7 | E7 | E7 | |

Verse 2
      E7
Yeah, back at the Roadhouse,

They got some bungalows.

Yeah, back at the Roadhouse,

They got some bungalows.

And that's for the people,

Who like to go down slow.

Bridge 1

A
Let it roll, baby roll,

Let it roll, baby roll,

Let it roll, baby roll,

     B   C
Let it roll,

B   E7
All night long.

| E7 | E7 | E7 | E7 | |

Guitar Solo ‖: E7 | E7 | E7 | E7 :‖ *play 3 times*

Middle

     E7
You gotta roll, roll, roll,

You gotta thrill my soul alright.

Roll, roll, roll, roll,

A-through my soul,

I gotta peep-a con-ya chou chum,

Paw cork, cork.

I gotta hay-cha coon-a may-cha,

Ba-ba loo-la hay chow,

Bow-pa key chow,

Ee sown comp

Yeah, right.

Ashen lady, ashen lady.

Give up your vows,

Give up your vows.

Save our city,

Save our city.

Right now.

Verse 3
               E⁷
Well, I woke up this morning,

I got myself a beer.

Well, I woke up this morning,

And I got myself a beer.

The future's uncertain,

And the end is always near.

Bridge 2
              A
Let it roll, baby roll,

Let it roll, baby roll,

Let it roll, baby roll,
       B   **C**
Let it roll,
C♯ D   **D♯ E**
All night long.

She Caught The Katy
(And Left Me A Mule To Ride)

Words & Music by
Taj Mahal & James Rachel

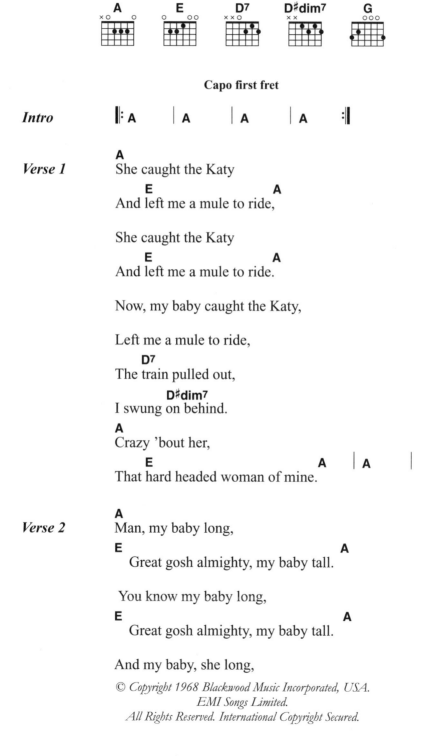

Capo first fret

Intro ‖: A | A | A | A :‖

Verse 1

    A
She caught the Katy
    E   **A**
And left me a mule to ride,

She caught the Katy
    E   **A**
And left me a mule to ride.

Now, my baby caught the Katy,

Left me a mule to ride,
   D7
The train pulled out,
      D♯dim7
I swung on behind.
A
Crazy 'bout her,
    E   **A** | **A** |
That hard headed woman of mine.

Verse 2

    A
Man, my baby long,
E   **A**
  Great gosh almighty, my baby tall.

 You know my baby long,
E   **A**
  Great gosh almighty, my baby tall.

And my baby, she long,

cont.   My baby, she tall,

       D⁷
She sleepin' with her head in the kitchen

           D♯dim7
And her feet's out in the hall,

A
Crazy 'bout her,

        E   **A D⁷ A**
That hard headed woman of mine.

        D⁷
Bridge   Well, I love my baby,

She's so fine,

A
  But I wish she'd come and see me some time.

          G
She don't be - lieve in our love, ah,

Look whatta hole I'm in.

         E
She don't be - lieve on sight,

Kid, look what shape I'm in.

Huh-huh.

Instrumental	A	E	A	A	
	A	E	A	A	
	A	E	A	A	
	A	A	D⁷	D♯dim7	
	A	E	D⁷	A	‖

Verse 3	**A** She caught the Katy
	E **A** And left me a mule to ride,
	She caught the Katy
	E **A** And left me a mule to ride.
	Well, my baby caught the Katy,
	Left me a mule to ride,
	D⁷ The train pulled out,
	D♯dim7 I swung on behind.
	A Crazy 'bout her,
	E That hard headed woman,
	D⁷ Hard headed woman of mine.

Link   **A**
‖: Huh-huh, huh-huh :‖
     (2° Tacet vocal)

Outro   ‖: **A** | **E** | **A** | **A**   :‖ *Repeat to fade*

Shake It And Break It
(But Don't Let It Fall Mama)

Words & Music by
Charley Patton

F   C7   Gm   C7/E

(chord diagrams: F, C7, Gm fr3, C7/E)

Intro

| F | C7 | F | C7 | |

| F | C7 | F | Gm F |

| C7/E F | C7 | F | C7 | |

| F | C7 | F | Gm F | C7/E F ‖

Chorus 1

        C7
You can shake it, you can break it, you can hang it on the wall,

F
Throw it out the window, catch it 'fore it fall.

        C7
You can   shake it, you can break it, you can hang it on the wall,

F
It out the window, catch it 'fore it falls?

    Gm   F   C7/E   F
My jelly, my roll, sweet mama, don't let it fall.

Verse 1

C7   F
Ev'rybody have a jelly roll like mine, I lives in town,

   C7   F
I,   ain't got no brown, I, and I want it now.

    Gm   F   C7/E   F
My jelly, my roll, sweet mama, don't let it fall.

Chorus 2

       C7
You can snatch it, you can grab it, you can break it,

        F
You can twist it any way that I love to get it.

C7   F
I,   had my right mind since I, I blowed this town.

    Gm   F   C7/E   F
My jelly, my roll, sweet mama, don't let it fall.

Chorus 3	As Chorus 1

Verse 2

   C7   **F**
I ain't got nobody here but me and myself,
   C7   **F**
I,   stay blue all the time, aw, when the sun goes down.
     Gm   **F**   **C7/E**   **F**
My jelly, my roll, sweet mama, don't let it fall.

Chorus 4	As Chorus 1

Chorus 5

            C7
You can snatch it, you can grab it,

You can break it, you can twist it,
F
Any way that I love to get it.
C7   **F**
I, had my right mind, I,   be worried sometime.
     Gm   **F**   **C7/E**   **F**
'Bout a jelly, my roll, sweet mama, don't let it fall.

Chorus 6	As Chorus 1

Verse 3

   C7   **F**
I know I been to town, I, I walked around,
   C7   **F**
I, start leavin' town, I, I fool around.
     Gm   **F**   **C7/E**   **F**
My jelly, my roll, sweet mama don't let it fall.

Chorus 7	As Chorus 1

Outro

     C7
Jus' shake it, you can break it, you can hang it on the wall,
F
It out the window, catch it 'for it falls?
     Gm   **F**   **C7/E**   **F**
My jelly, my roll, sweet mama, don't let it.

Sittin' On Top Of The World

Words & Music by
Walter Jacobs & Lonnie Carter

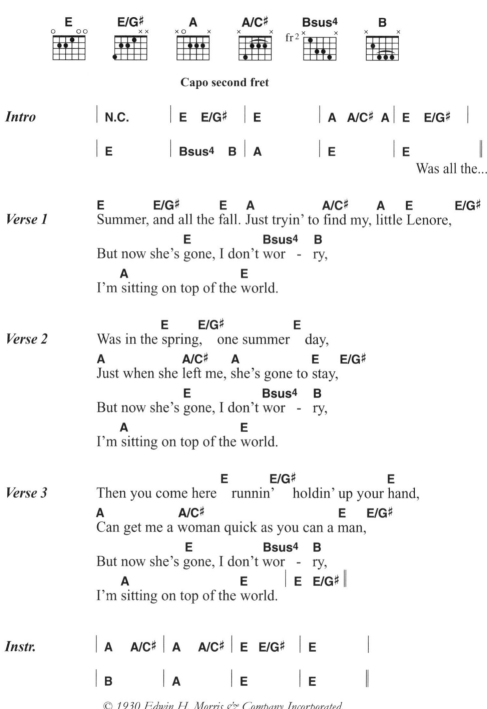

Capo second fret

Intro | N.C. | E E/G♯ | E | A A/C♯ A | E E/G♯ |
| E | Bsus4 B | A | E | E ‖

Was all the...

Verse 1
E E/G♯ E A   A/C♯ A E E/G♯
Summer, and all the fall. Just tryin' to find my, little Lenore,
      E   Bsus4 B
But now she's gone, I don't wor - ry,
 A   E
I'm sitting on top of the world.

Verse 2
     E E/G♯   E
Was in the spring, one summer day,
A   A/C♯ A   E E/G♯
Just when she left me, she's gone to stay,
      E   Bsus4 B
But now she's gone, I don't wor - ry,
 A   E
I'm sitting on top of the world.

Verse 3
       E E/G♯   E
Then you come here runnin' holdin' up your hand,
A   A/C♯   E E/G♯
Can get me a woman quick as you can a man,
      E   Bsus4 B
But now she's gone, I don't wor - ry,
  A   E | E E/G♯ ‖
I'm sitting on top of the world.

Instr. | A A/C♯ | A A/C♯ | E E/G♯ | E |
| B | A | E | E ‖

Verse 4

              E   E/G♯   E
It have been days   I didn't know your name,

             A   A/C♯   A   E   E/G♯
Why should I worry   and prayer in vain?

             E   Bsus4 B
But now she's gone, I don't wor - ry,

   A   E
I'm sitting on top of the world.

Verse 5

             E   E/G♯   E
Going to the   station,   down in the yard,

A   A/C♯   A
Going get me a freight train,

            E   E/G♯
Worked some, got hard.

             E   Bsus4 B
But now she's gone, I don't wor - ry,

   A   E
I'm sitting on top of the world.

Verse 6

             E   E/G♯   E
The lonesome days,   they have gone by,

A   A/C♯   A   E   E/G♯
Why should you beg me and say good - bye?

            E   Bsus4 B
But now she's gone, I don't wor - ry,

   A   E
I'm sitting on top of the world.

Smokestack Lightning

Words & Music by
Chester Burnette

E

| Intro | | E | | E | | E | | E | | E | | E | |

Verse 1

E
   Ah-oh, smokestack lightnin,

Shinin', just like gold,

Why don't ya hear me cryin'?

A-whoo-hoo, whoo,

Whoo.

Verse 2

E
   Whoa-oh, tell me, baby,

What's the, matter with you?

Why don't ya hear me cryin'?

Whoo-hooo, whoo-hoo,

Whoo.

Harmonica solo

| | E | | E | | E | | E | | E | | E | |

Verse 3

E

Whoa-oh, tell me, baby,

Where did ya stay last night?

A-why don't ya hear me cryin'?

Whoo-hoo, whoo-hoo,

Whoo.

Verse 4

E

Whoa-oh, stop your train,

Let her go for a ride.

Why don't ya hear me cryin'?

Whoo-hoo, whoo-hoo,

Whoo.

Harmonica solo 2

| E | | E | | E | | E | | E | | E | ‖

Verse 5

E

Whoa-oh, fare ya well.

Never see, a-you no more.

A-why don't ya hear me cryin'?

Whoo-hoo, whoo-hoo,

Whoo.

Verse 6

E

Whoa-oh, who been here baby since,

I-I been gone, a little, bity boy?

Girl, be on.

A-whoo-hoo, whoo-hoo,

Whoo.

To fade

Smoking Gun

Words & Music by
Robert Cray, David Amy & Richard Cousins

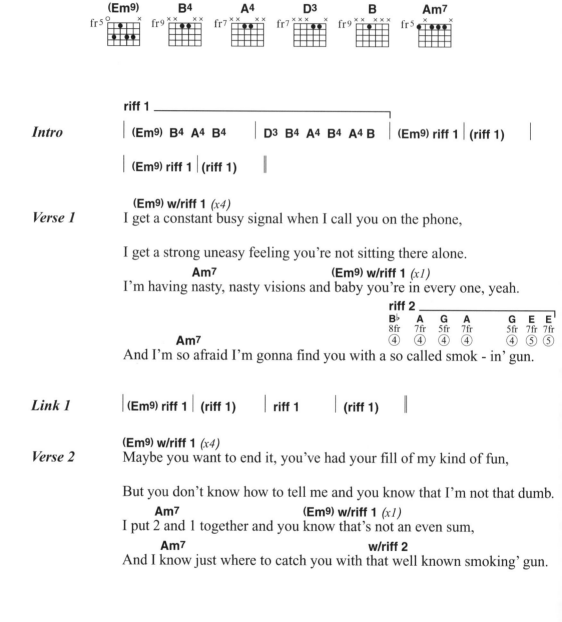

Intro

| (Em9) B4 A4 B4 | D3 B4 A4 B4 A4 B | (Em9) riff 1 | (riff 1) |

| (Em9) riff 1 | (riff 1) |

Verse 1

(Em9) w/riff 1 *(x4)*
I get a constant busy signal when I call you on the phone,

I get a strong uneasy feeling you're not sitting there alone.

Am7 (Em9) w/riff 1 *(x1)*
I'm having nasty, nasty visions and baby you're in every one, yeah.

Am7
And I'm so afraid I'm gonna find you with a so called smok - in' gun.

Link 1

| (Em9) riff 1 | (riff 1) | riff 1 | (riff 1) |

Verse 2

(Em9) w/riff 1 *(x4)*
Maybe you want to end it, you've had your fill of my kind of fun,

But you don't know how to tell me and you know that I'm not that dumb.

Am7 (Em9) w/riff 1 *(x1)*
I put 2 and 1 together and you know that's not an even sum,

Am7 w/riff 2
And I know just where to catch you with that well known smoking' gun.

Solo   ‖: **(Em9) w/riff 1** | **(riff 1)** | **riff 1** | **(riff 1)** |

         | **riff 1** | **(riff 1)** | **riff 1** | **(riff 1)** |

         | **riff 1** | **(riff 1)** | **riff 1** | **(riff 1)** |

         | **Am7** | **Am7** | **(Em9) w/riff 1** | **(riff 1)** |

         | **Am7** | **Am7** | **riff 2** :‖

         | **(Em9) w/riff 1** | **(riff 1)** | **riff 1** | **(riff 1)** ‖

         (Em9) w/riff 1 *(x4)*

Verse 3   I'm standing here bewildered, I can't remember just what I've done,

         I can hear the sirens whining, my eyes blinded by the sun.

         Am7   **(Em9) w/riff 1** *(x1)*
         I know that I should be running, my heart's beating just like a drum.

               Am7
         Now they've knocked me down and taken it,

         w/riff 2 | **(Em9) w/riff 1** | **(riff 1)** ‖
         That still hot and smokin' gun.

         w/riff 1
Outro   ‖: Yeah, still hot smokin' gun, they've taken it.

         Still hot smokin' gun oh, they've taken it.

         Still hot smokin' gun, knocked me down, taken it. :‖ *Repeat to fade*
                                                          w/vox + Gtr. ad lib.

So Many Roads, So Many Trains

Words & Music by
Marshall Paul

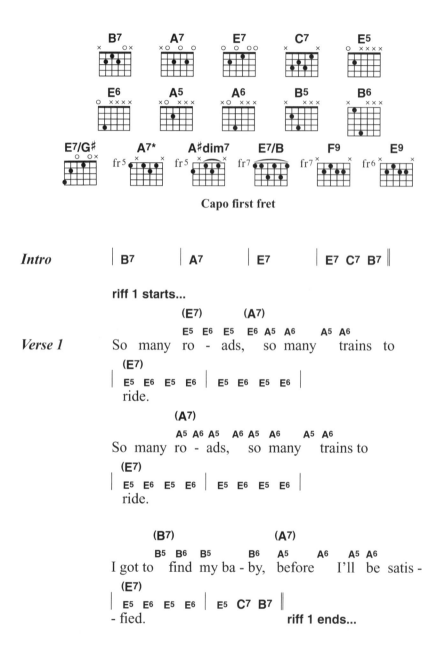

Capo first fret

Intro | B7 | A7 | E7 | E7 C7 B7 ‖

riff 1 starts...

             (E7)   (A7)
             E5 E6 E5   E6 A5 A6   A5 A6
Verse 1   So many ro - ads,   so many   trains to
            (E7)
            | E5 E6 E5 E6 | E5 E6 E5 E6 |
            ride.

                    (A7)
                    A5 A6 A5   A6 A5 A6   A5 A6
            So many ro - ads,   so many   trains to
            (E7)
            | E5 E6 E5 E6 | E5 E6 E5 E6 |
            ride.

                (B7)   (A7)
                B5 B6 B5   B6 A5   A6   A5 A6
            I got to   find my ba - by, before   I'll be satis -
                (E7)
            | E5 E6 E5 E6 | E5 C7 B7 ‖
            - fied.   **riff 1 ends...**

Verse 2

(E7)w/riff 1   A7   E7

Well, I was standing at my window, when I heard that whistle blow.

A7   E7

Oh, I was standing at my window, when I heard that whistle blow.

      B7   A7   E7   C7   B7 ‖

Yes it sounded like a straight-line, oh but it was a P&O.

Solo

| E7w/riff 1 | A7 | | E7 | | E7 | |
| B7 | A7 | | E7 | | E7 B7 ‖

| E7w/riff 1 | A7 | E7 | E7 | |
| A7 | A7 | E7 | E7 | |
| B7 | A7 | E7 | E7 B7 ‖

Verse 3

(E7)w/riff 1   A7   E7

It was a mean old fireman and a cruel old engin - eer.

A7   E7

Oh, a mean old fireman and a cruel old engin - eer.

      B7   A7 N.C.

Yeah, it's taken my baby   yeah it's left me standing

E7   E7/G♯   A7*   A♯dim7 | E7/B   F9   E9 ‖

here.

153

Stack O'Lee Blues

Traditional
Arranged by John Hurt

Eadd⁹   E*   E   A⁶   A   B

Tune guitar down a semitone

Intro

| Eadd⁹ E* E Eadd⁹ E* | Eadd⁹ E* E |

| Eadd⁹ E* E Eadd⁹ E* | Eadd⁹ E* E |

| A⁶ A | A⁶ A | A | E | |

| B | B | Eadd⁹ E* E ‖

Verse 1

        E
Po - lice officer, how can it be?
          A   E
You can 'rest ev'rybody but cruel Stack O' Lee.
        B   E
That bad man, oh, cruel Stack O' Lee.

Link 1

| Eadd⁹ E* E Eadd⁹ E* | Eadd⁹ E* E |

| Eadd⁹ E* E Eadd⁹ E* | Eadd⁹ E* E |

| A⁶ A | A⁶ A | A | E | |

| B | B | Eadd⁹ E* E ‖

Verse 2

   E
Billy de Lyon told Stack O' Lee, "Please don't take my life,
     A   E
I got two little babies, and a darlin' lovin' wife."
       B   E
That bad man, oh, cruel Stack O' Lee.

Link 2   As Link 1

Verse 3

E
"What I care about your two little babies, your darlin' lovin' wife?
                    A   E
You done stole my Stetson hat, I'm bound to take your life."
              B   E
That bad man, oh cruel Stack O' Lee.

Link 3
w/vocal ad lib.

‖: Eadd⁹ E* E Eadd⁹ E* | Eadd⁹ E* E |

| Eadd⁹ E* E Eadd⁹ E* | Eadd⁹ E* E |

| A⁶   A | A⁶   A | A | E |

| B | B | Eadd⁹ E* E | E   :‖

Verse 4

(E)
Boom boom, boom boom, with the forty-four,
              A   E
When I spied Billy de Lyon, he was lyin' down on the floor
              B   E
That bad man, oh cruel Stack O' Lee.

Link 4   As Link 1

Verse 5

E
"Gentleman's of the jury, what do you think of that?
              A   E
Stack O' Lee killed Billy de Lyon about a five-dollar Stetson hat."
                B   E
That bad man, oh cruel Stack O' Lee.

Link 5   As Link 1

Verse 6

              E
Standin' on the gallows, head way up high,
        A   E
At twelve o'clock they killed him, they's all glad to see him die.
                B   E
That bad man, oh, cruel Stack O' Lee.

Outro   As Link 1

Statesboro Blues

Words & Music by
Willie McTell

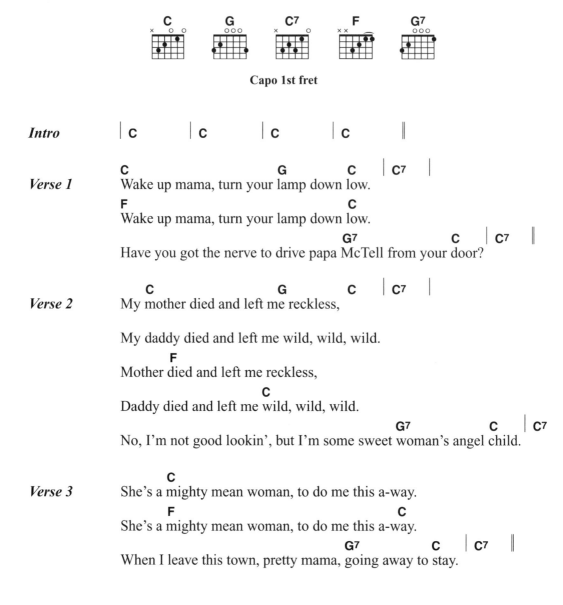

Capo 1st fret

Intro | C | C | C | C   ‖

Verse 1
C   G   C | C7 |
Wake up mama, turn your lamp down low.
F   C
Wake up mama, turn your lamp down low.
                                    G7   C | C7   ‖
Have you got the nerve to drive papa McTell from your door?

Verse 2
C   G   C | C7 |
My mother died and left me reckless,

My daddy died and left me wild, wild, wild.
             F
Mother died and left me reckless,
                 C
Daddy died and left me wild, wild, wild.
                                    G7   C | C7   ‖
No, I'm not good lookin', but I'm some sweet woman's angel child.

Verse 3
             C
She's a mighty mean woman, to do me this a-way.
             F   C
She's a mighty mean woman, to do me this a-way.
                                    G7   C | C7   ‖
When I leave this town, pretty mama, going away to stay.

Verse 4

        C   **C7**
I once loved a woman, better than I'd ever seen.

        F   **C**
I once loved a woman, better than I'd ever seen.

                                  G7   **C** | **C7** ‖
Treat me like I was a king and she was a doggone queen.

Verse 5

        C
Sis - ter, tell your Brother, Brother tell your Auntie, Auntie, tell your Uncle,

                            C7
Uncle tell my Cousin, Cousin tell my friend,

F   **C**
Goin' up the country, Mama, don't you want to go?

                          G7   **C** | **C7** ‖
May take me a fair brown, may take me one or two more.

Verse 6

        C
Big Eighty left Savannah, Lord, and did not stop,

You ought to saw that coloured fireman when he got that boiler hot.

F   **C**
You can reach over in the corner mama and hand me my travelin' shoes.

                          G7   **C** | **C7** ‖
You know by that, I got them Statesboro' blues.

Verse 7

           C   **C7**
Mama, Sis - ter got 'em, Dad - dy got 'em,

Brother got 'em, friend got 'em, I got 'em,

        F   **C**
I Woke up this morning, we had them Statesboro' blues.

I looked over in the corner,

            C7   **C** | **C** | **G7** | **C C7**‖
Grandma and Grandpa had 'em too.

Susie Q

Words & Music by
Dale Hawkins, Stan Lewis & Eleanor Broadwater

Intro

Drums
4

riff 1

E	D	A	G	E		E	D	B	D	E
open	3fr	2fr	open	2fr		2fr	open	2fr	open	2fr
⑥	②	③	③	④		④	④	⑤	④	④

E7

Verse 1

(riff 1)   **w/riff 1** *(x1)*
    Oh, Susie-Q.

        A7
Oh, Susie-Q, how I love you,

C7   **B7**   **w/riff 1** *(x3)*
    My Susie-Q.

I like the way you walk,

I like the way you talk.

             A7
I like the way you walk,

I like the way you talk.

C7   **B7**   **(E5)**
    My Susie-Q.

Instr 1

(E5)	(E5)	E7	E7	
E7	E7	A7	A7	
A7	A7	B7	B7	
(E5)	(E5)	E7 w/riff 1	(riff 1)	

Verse 2

E7 w/riff 1 *(x2)*
Oh, Susie-Q.

Oh, Susie-Q.

       A7
Oh, Susie-Q.

Baby, how I love you,
C7   **B7 w/riff 1** *(x3)*
  My Susie-Q.

Well, say that you'll be true,

Well, say that you'll be true,

             A7
Well, say that you'll be true,

And never leave me blue.
C7   **B7**   **(E5)**
  My Susie-Q.

Instr 2

(E5)	(E5)	E7	E7	
A7	A7	B7	B7	
(E5)	

Verse 3

(E5)   **E7 w/riff 1** *(x2)*
  Oh, Susie-Q,

Oh, Susie-Q,

      A7
Oh, Susie-Q,

How I love you,
C7   **B7**
  My Susie Q.

Outro

‖: E7 w/riff 1 | (riff 1) :‖ *Repeat to fade w/ad lib. guitar*

Sweet Home Chicago

Words & Music by
Robert Johnson

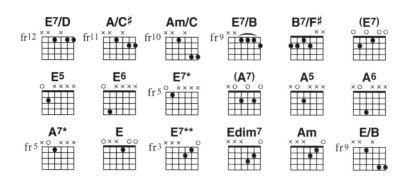

Capo 1st fret

Intro

| E⁷/D A/C♯ Am/C E⁷/B | E⁷/B   B7/F* ‖

riff 1 starts…
(E7)

Fig. 1 ⌐──────┐

Verse 1

E5 E6 E5 E6   A5   A6   A7*   A6   E5 E6 E5 E6 E7* E6 E5 E6
Oh,   baby don't you want to go?   Oh

(A7)   (E7)

Fig. 2 ⌐──────┐

A5 A6 A7* A6 A7   A6   A7*   A6   E5 E6 E5 E6
    Baby don't you   want to go,

Fig. 3 ⌐──────┐
{ **B** 7fr ① }
{ **C** 8fr ② ¼↗ } x5

E5 E6 E5 E6 B7/F♯
    Back to the land of California, to my sweet home Chicago?

| E E7** Edim⁷ Am E7 | E⁷/B   B7/F* ‖

…riff 1 ends

(E7) (B7)

Verse 2

    w/riff 1   **(E7)**
Oh, baby don't you want to go?

(A7)   **(E7)**
Oh baby don't you want to go,

             B7/F♯   **w/fig. 3**
Back to the land of California, to my sweet home Chicago?

| E E7** Edim7 Am E7 | E7/B   B7/F*   ‖ |

riff 2 starts…

    (E7)

Verse 3

    w/fig. 1 *(x4)*
Now, one and one is two. Two and two is four.

I'm heavy loaded baby, I'm booked, I gotta go.

    (A7)   **(A7)**
    w/fig. 2 *(x2)*   **w/fig. 1** *(x2)*
Cryin' baby, honey don't you want to go,

             B7/F♯   **w/fig. 3**
Back to the land of California, to my sweet home Chicago?

| E E7** Edim7 Am E | E   B7/F♯   ‖ |

                                        …riff 2 ends

    w/riff 1

Verse 4
Now, two and two is four, four and two is six.

You goin' keep on monkeyin' round here friend-boy,

Goin' get your business all in a trick.

             (A7)   **E7**
But I'm cryin' baby, honey don't you want to go,

             B7/F♯   **w/fig. 3**
Back to the land of California, to my sweet home Chicago?

| E E7** Edim7 Am E7 | E   B7/F♯   ‖ |

(**E7**)
w/riff 1

Verse 5   Now, six and two is eight, and eight and two is ten.

Friend-boy, she trick you one time, she sure gon' to do it again.
             (**A7**)   (**B7**)
But I'm cryin' hey, hey, baby don't you want to go,
                        w/riff 3
To the land of California, to my sweet home Chicago?

| E E7** Edim7 Am E7 | E   B7/F♯   ‖

(**E7**)
w/fig.1 *(x4)*

Verse 6   I'm goin' to California, from there to Des Moines, I 'way.

Somebody will tell me that you need my help someday.
             (**E7**)   (**E7**)
             w/fig.2*(x2)*   **w/fig.1** *(x2)*
Cryin', hey, hey, baby don't you want to go,
        B7/F*   **w/fig.3**
Back to the land of California, to my sweet home Chicago?

$\frac{2}{4}$| E/B $\frac{4}{4}$| E7/D A/C♯ Am/C | E/B   E7/B   ‖

Tattoo'd Lady

Words & Music by
Rory Gallagher

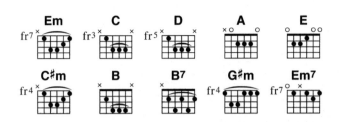

Intro ‖ *Sound fx* ‖

Verse 1

     Em   C   D   Em
Tattoo'd lady,   bearded baby, they're my fami - ly.

                       C   D   Em
When I was lonely,   something told me, where I could always be.

Where I could wish for pennies,
 C   D   Em
If you got any, you'd meet me down at the shooting galle - ry.

You know I'm a fairground baby,
 C   D   Em
   Wonder what made me, fall for the Pearly Queen.

Chorus 1

       A   E
Well I spent my youth, under canvas roof,
            C♯m   B E
As I roamed from town to town.
      A   E
I'm not fooling, when I say I got no schoolin',
C♯m   B7
Never like the class bell sound.
      A   C♯m
From inside the caravan, I hear the fairground band,
G♯m   B
Sounding good as they can be.
       A   C♯m
You know I can't be found, but if you look around,
G♯m   B
Tomorrow we'll be gone by dawn. Ah yeah.

Instr.

```
‖: Em      | C        | D          | Em       :‖
 | A        | E        | E C♯m B | E       |
 | A        | E        | C♯m     | B7       |
‖: A        | C♯m     | G♯m      | B        :‖
```

Verse 2

             Em
I hear it on the loudspeaker say,
C   **D**   **Em**
The fire eater is a real fine sight to see,

                                 C
You know he's a death cheater, some kind of central heater,
        D   **Em**
Be sure to save a seat for me.
                  Em   **C**
Let me tell you about wicked Sadie, she's no baby,
      D   **Em**
The law came, and tried to close her sideshow down.

But soon she had the D.A. cheering,
C   **D**   **Em**
   The police chief wearing, her garter for a crown.

Chorus 2

     A   **E**
I spent my youth, under canvas roof,
               C♯m   **B** **E**
As I roamed from town to town.
      A   **E**
I'm not fooling, when I say I got no schoolin',
C♯m   **B7**
Never like the school bell sound.
      A   **C♯m**
From the caravan, I hear the fairground band,
G♯m   **B**
Sounding really good, as they can   be.
      A   **C♯m**
You know I can't be found, but if you look around,
   G♯m   **B**
To - morrow I'll be gone by dawn.

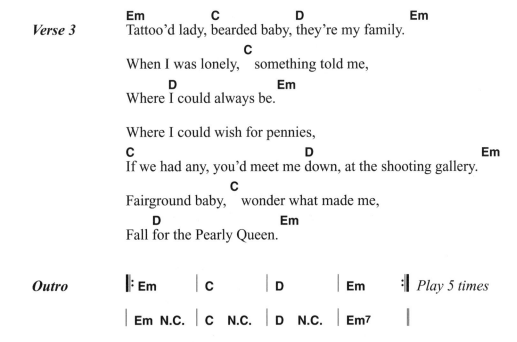

Verse 3

Em   C   D   Em

Tattoo'd lady, bearded baby, they're my family.

                     C

When I was lonely,   something told me,

        D   Em

Where I could always be.

Where I could wish for pennies,

C   D   Em

If we had any, you'd meet me down, at the shooting gallery.

                     C

Fairground baby,   wonder what made me,

        D   Em

Fall for the Pearly Queen.

Outro

‖: Em | C | D | Em   :‖ *Play 5 times*

| Em N.C. | C N.C. | D N.C. | Em7 ‖

That's All Right Mama

Words & Music by
Arthur Crudup

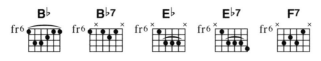

Tune guitar slightly flat

* Implied harmony throughout

Intro | *B♭ | B♭7 | E♭ E♭7 | E♭ E♭7 | B♭ E♭ | B♭ |

Verse 1
                      B♭
Well now, that's all right now mama, that's all right for you,
                                     B♭7
That's all right mama, anyway you do.
                E♭ **E♭7**   **E♭** **E♭7**
But that's all right,   that's all right,
              F7   **B♭ E♭** | **B♭ F7** ‖
That's all right now mama, anyway you do.

Verse 2
                      B♭ N.C.   **B♭ N.C.**
Well my Mama she done told me, Papa told me too,
        B♭ N.C.   **B♭7**
The   life you're living, son, now wo - men be the death of you.
                E♭ **E♭7**   **E♭** **E♭7**
But that's all right,   that's all right,
              F7   **B♭ E♭** | **B♭ F7** ‖
That's all right now Mama, anyway you do.

Instr. 1 | B♭ | B♭ | B♭ | B♭7 |

          | E♭ E♭7 | E♭ E♭7 | B♭ E♭ | B♭ F7 ‖

Verse 3

B♭ N.C.　　　　　　　**B♭ N.C.**
Baby, one and one is two, two and two is four,

　B♭ N.C.　　　　　　　　**B♭7**
I love that woman but I got to let her go.

　　　　E♭　**E♭7**　　　**E♭**　**E♭7**
That's all right,　　that's all right,

　　F7　　　　　　　　　　　**B♭**　**E♭**　|　**B♭**　**F7**　‖
That's all right now Mama, anyway you do.

Verse 4

　　　B♭ N.C.　　　　　　　**B♭ N.C.**
Babe, now if you don't want me, why not tell me so,

　B♭ N.C.　　　　　　　　　**B♭7**
You won't be bothered with me round your house no more.

　　　　E♭　**E♭7**　　　**E♭**　**E♭7**
That's all right,　　that's all right,

　　F7　　　　　　　　　　　**B♭**　**E♭**　|　**B♭**　**F7**　‖
That's all right now Mama, anyway you do.

Instr. 2　　　As Instr. 1

Outro

| **B♭** | **B♭** | **B♭** | |
De cra de de de de.　De de de de.　　　De de de de.

| **B♭** | **B♭** | **B♭** | |
De de de de.　　De de de de.　　　De de de. Now that's al -

| **E♭**　**E♭7** | **E♭**　**B♭** | **F7** | |
right　　That's al - right　　That's al - right now mama,

| **F7** | **B♭** | **B♭** | ‖
any way you　　　do

The Things That I Used To Do

Words & Music by
Eddie Jones

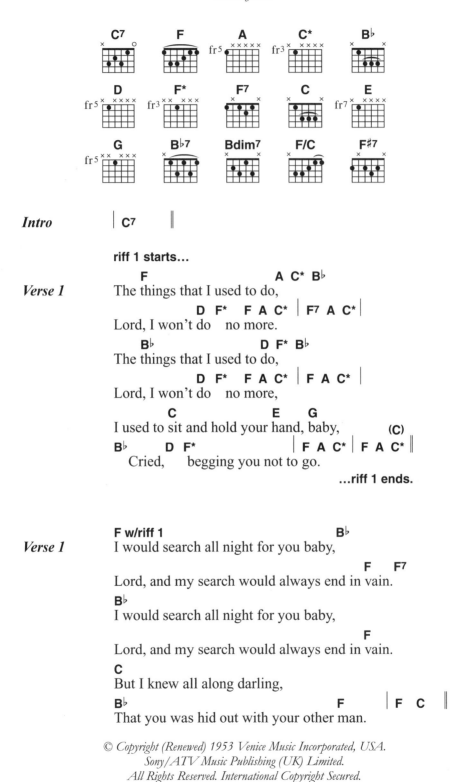

Intro | C7 ‖

riff 1 starts…

                F   A C* B♭
Verse 1   The things that I used to do,
                              D F*   F A C* | F7 A C* |
              Lord, I won't do   no more.
                  B♭   D F* B♭
              The things that I used to do,
                              D F*   F A C* | F A C* |
              Lord, I won't do   no more,
                        C   E   G
              I used to sit and hold your hand, baby,   **(C)**
              B♭   D F* | F A C* | F A C* ‖
                 Cried,   begging you not to go.

                                                …riff 1 ends.

              F w/riff 1   B♭
Verse 1   I would search all night for you baby,
                                                    F   F7
              Lord, and my search would always end in vain.
              B♭
              I would search all night for you baby,
                                                    F
              Lord, and my search would always end in vain.
              C
              But I knew all along darling,
              B♭   F | F C ‖
              That you was hid out with your other man.

Instr. | (F)w/riff 1 | B♭ | F | F7 |

| B♭ | B♭ | F | F |

| C | B♭ | F   ‖

                                        F w/riff 1

Verse 3   I'm going to send you back to your mother, baby,

        B♭   **F**

Lord, and I'm going back to my family too.

F7   **B♭**

  I'm going to send you back to your mother, baby,

                                F

Lord, and I'm going back to my family too.

       C

'Cause nothing I do that please you baby,

B♭   **F B♭7 Bdim7** | **F/C F♯7 F7** ‖

  Lord, I just can't get along with you.

The Thrill Is Gone

Words & Music by
Roy Hawkins & Rick Darnell

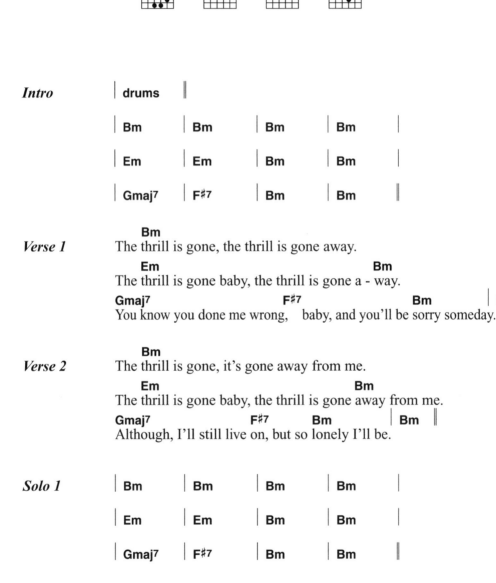

Intro

| drums ‖

| Bm | Bm | Bm | Bm |

| Em | Em | Bm | Bm |

| Gmaj7 | F#7 | Bm | Bm ‖

Verse 1

Bm
The thrill is gone, the thrill is gone away.

Em   Bm
The thrill is gone baby, the thrill is gone a - way.

Gmaj7   F#7   Bm | Bm ‖
You know you done me wrong,   baby, and you'll be sorry someday.

Verse 2

Bm
The thrill is gone, it's gone away from me.

Em   Bm
The thrill is gone baby, the thrill is gone away from me.

Gmaj7   F#7   Bm | Bm ‖
Although, I'll still live on, but so lonely I'll be.

Solo 1

| Bm | Bm | Bm | Bm |

| Em | Em | Bm | Bm |

| Gmaj7 | F#7 | Bm | Bm ‖

Verse 3

Bm
The thrill is gone, it's gone away for good.

Em   **Bm**
Oh, the thrill is gone baby, it's gone away for good.

Gmaj⁷   **F♯7**
Someday I know I'll be holding on,   baby,

               Bm | **Bm** ‖
Just like I know a good man should.

Verse 4

Bm
You know I'm free, free now baby, I'm free from your spell.

Em   **Bm**
Oh, I'm free, free, free now, I'm free from your spell.

    Gmaj⁷   **F♯7**   **Bm** | **Bm** ‖
And now that it's all   over, All I can do is wish you well.

Solo 2   As Solo 1

Outro   ‖: **Bm** | **Bm**   :‖ *Repeat to fade*

Tuff Enuff

Words & Music by
Kim Wilson

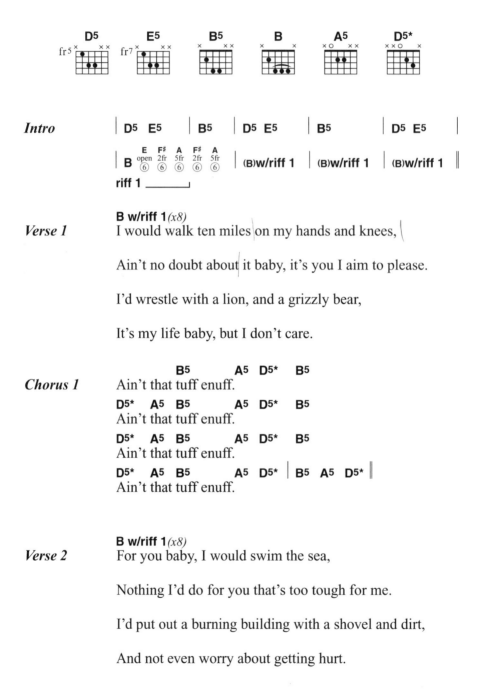

Intro
| D5 E5 | B5 | D5 E5 | B5 | D5 E5 |

| B | (B)w/riff 1 | (B)w/riff 1 | (B)w/riff 1 ‖

riff 1 _____

Verse 1

B w/riff 1 *(x8)*
I would walk ten miles on my hands and knees,

Ain't no doubt about it baby, it's you I aim to please.

I'd wrestle with a lion, and a grizzly bear,

It's my life baby, but I don't care.

Chorus 1

          B5   **A5 D5*** **B5**
Ain't that tuff enuff.
D5* **A5 B5**   **A5 D5*** **B5**
Ain't that tuff enuff.
D5* **A5 B5**   **A5 D5*** **B5**
Ain't that tuff enuff.
D5* **A5 B5**   **A5 D5*** | **B5 A5 D5*** ‖
Ain't that tuff enuff.

Verse 2

B w/riff 1 *(x8)*
For you baby, I would swim the sea,

Nothing I'd do for you that's too tough for me.

I'd put out a burning building with a shovel and dirt,

And not even worry about getting hurt.

Chorus 2   As Chorus 1

Link 1 | **D5** | **D5** | **B5** | **B5** |

              | **D5** | **D5** **E5** | **B5** | **B5** ‖

B w/riff 1 *(x8)*

Verse 3   I'd work twenty-four hours, seven days a week,

Just so I could come home and kiss your cheek.

I love you in the morning, and I love you at noon,

I love you in the night, and take you to the moon.

Chorus 3   As Chorus 1

B w/riff 1 *(x8)*

Verse 4   I'd lay in a pile of burning money that I've earned,

And not even worry about getting burned.

I'd climb the Empire State, fight Muhammad Ali,

Just to have you baby, close to me.

Link 2   As Link 1

Chorus 4   As Chorus 1

              D5

Chorus 5   ‖: Ain't that tuff enuff.

Ain't that tuff enuff. :‖   *Repeat to fade*

Voodoo Child (Slight Return)

Words & Music by
Jimi Hendrix

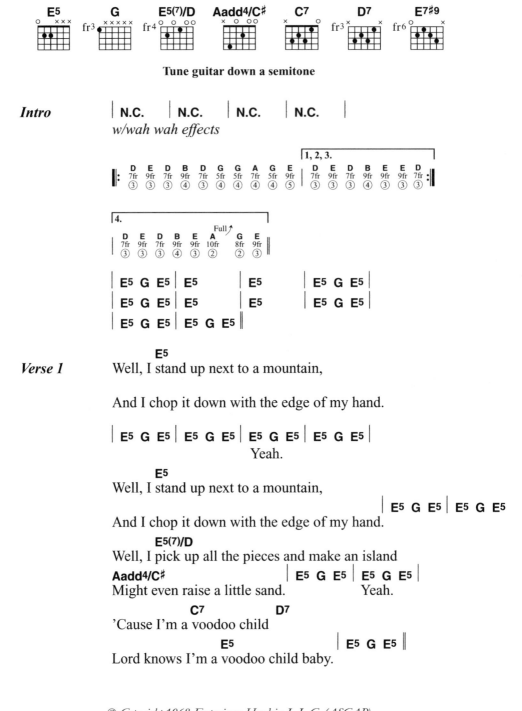

Tune guitar down a semitone

Intro
| N.C. | N.C. | N.C. | N.C. |

w/wah wah effects

Verse 1

E5
Well, I stand up next to a mountain,

And I chop it down with the edge of my hand.

| E5 G E5 | E5 G E5 | E5 G E5 | E5 G E5 |
Yeah.

E5
Well, I stand up next to a mountain,

| E5 G E5 | E5 G E5 |
And I chop it down with the edge of my hand.

E5(7)/D
Well, I pick up all the pieces and make an island

Aadd4/C# | E5 G E5 | E5 G E5 |
Might even raise a little sand.   Yeah.

C7   D7
'Cause I'm a voodoo child

E5 | E5 G E5 ||
Lord knows I'm a voodoo child baby.

Link 1

| E5 | E5 | E5 | E5 | |

| E5 | E5 | E5 G E5 | E5 G E5 |

| E5 | E5 | E5 | E5 | |

| E5 G E5 | E5 G E5 | E5 G E5 | E5 G E5 ‖

Verse 2

E5 | E5 G E5 | E5 G E5 |
I want to say one more last thing,

E5 G E5
          I didn't mean to take up all your sweet time.

        E5 G E5 | E5 G E5 | E5 G E5 |
I'll give it right   back to you one of these days.

| E5 G E5 | E5 G E5 |
Ha ha ha.

E5 G   E5
          I said I didn't mean to take up all your sweet time

E5 G   E5   E5 G   E5
          I'll give it right back one of these days.

E5 G   E5   E5(7)/D
          If I don't meet you no more in this world then, uh,

Aadd4/C♯   E5 G E5   E5 G E5
I'll meet you on the next one and don't be late,   don't be late.

              C7   D7
'Cause I'm a voodoo child, voodoo child,

              E7♯9
Lord knows I'm a voodoo child. Hey, hey, hey.

Link 2

| E5 | E5 | E5 | E5 |
             I'm a voodoo child baby.   I don't take no for an

| E5 | E5 | E5 | E5   ‖
  answer.   Questions no.

‖: E5 | E5 | E5 | E5   :‖ *Repeat to fade w/ad lib.*

Wang Dang Doodle

Words & Music by
Willie Dixon

Em

fr12

Tune Guitar down a semitone

riff 1

Intro

(Em)   **(Em)**

E	A	B	D	B	E	D	E	G	E	D	E
12fr	12fr	14fr	12fr	14fr	14fr	12fr	12fr	10fr	12fr	10fr	12fr
⑥	⑤	⑤	④	⑤	④	④	⑥	⑤	⑥	⑥	⑥

w/riff 1

| **(Em)** | **(Em)** |

Verse 1

(Em)w/riff 1 *(x8)*
Tell Automatic Slim, tell Razor Totin' Jim,

Tell Butcher Knife Totin' Annie, tell Fast Talking Fanny.

We gonna pitch a ball, a down to that union hall,

We gonna romp and tromp till midnight,

We gonna fuss and fight till daylight.

Chorus 1

(Em)w/riff 1 *(x8)*
We gonna pitch a wang dang doodle all night long.

All night long, all night long, all night long, all night long.

We gonna pitch a wang dang doodle all night long.

Verse 2

(Em)**w/riff 1** *(x8)*
Tell Kudu-Crawlin' Red, tell Abyssinian Ned,

Tell old Pistol Pete, tell everybody he meet.

Tonight we need no rest, we really gonna throw a mess,

We gonna to knock down all of the windows,

We gonna kick down all the doors.

Chorus 2   As Chorus 1

w/riff 1_____

Solo   ‖: Em | Em   :‖ *Play 8 times*

Verse 3

(Em)**w/riff 1** *(x8)*
Tell Fats and Washboard Sam, that everybody gonna to jam,

Tell Shaky and Boxcar Joe, we got sawdust on the floor.

Tell Peg and Caroline Dye, we gonna have a heck of a time,

When the fish scent fill the air, there'll be snuff juice everywhere.

Chorus 3   As Chorus 1. *To fade.*

West Side Baby

Words & Music by
John Cameron & Dallas Bartley

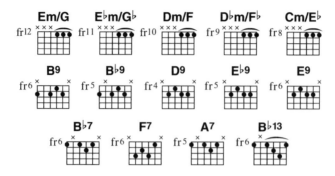

Intro

| Em/G E♭m/G♭ Dm/F D♭m/F♭ Cm/E♭ ‖

Verse 1

B9 B♭9   D9 E♭9   B♭7
   I've got a west side baby, she lives way across town.

D9 E♭9   E9 E♭9   B♭7
   I've got a west side baby, she lives way across town.

F7   E♭9   B♭7 E♭9 | B♭7 F7 ‖
And when I'm with my baby, I don't want a soul a - round.

Verse 2

B9 B♭9   E9 E♭9
   Now she's kind of tall and legged, she's always dresing swell.

B9 B♭9   A7 B♭9
   She sets my soul on fire, when she rang my front door bell.

E♭9   E9 E♭9   B♭9 B9 B♭9 | B♭7 F7 ‖
  Yes, I've got a west side ba - by, she lives way across town.

F7   E♭9   B♭7 E♭9 | B♭7 F7 ‖
And when I'm with my baby, I don't want a soul a - round.

Verse 3

B9 B♭9   E9 E♭9
  Now Monday morning ear - ly, someone bang upon my door.

B9 B♭9   B9 B♭9
  I knew it wasn't my ba - by, 'cause she's never knocked before.

E9 E♭9   E9 E♭9
  So I laid in bed and won - dered, who could the caller be.

B9 B♭9
  I thought it was the insurance man 'cause he's been heckling for me.

E♭9   B♭7
 Crazy about my west side baby, she lives way across town.

F7   E♭9   B♭7 E♭9 | B♭7 F7 B♭13 ‖
And when I'm with my baby, I don't want a soul a - round.

179

Where Did You Sleep Last Night?

Words & Music by
Huddie Ledbetter

Intro ‖: E7 E7/B | A G | B5 B5/F♯ | E7 E7/B :‖

Verse 1
    E7   E7/B   A   G
My girl, my girl, don't lie to me.
         B5   B5/F♯   E7   E7/B
Tell me where did you sleep last night? Come on, tell me baby.
     E7   E7/B   A   G
In the pines, in the pines where the sun don't ever shine,
     B5   B5/F♯   E7   E7/B
I would shiver the whole night through.

Verse 2
    E7   E7/B   A   G
My girl, my girl, where will you go?
     B5   B5/F♯   E7   E7/B
I'm going where the cold wind blows, where's that baby?
     E7   E7/B   A   G
In the pines, in the pines, where the sun don't ever shine,
     B5   B5/F♯   E7   E7/B
I would shiver the whole night through.

Verse 3
    E7   E7/B   A   G
My girl, my girl, don't you lie to me.
         B5   B5/F♯   E7
Tell me where did you sleep last night?
                 E7/B
Come on and tell me something about it.
     E7   E7/B   A   G
In the pines, in the pines, where the sun don't ever shine,
     B5   B5/F♯   E7   E7/B
I would shiver the whole night through, shiver for me now.

Instr. | E⁷ E⁷/B | A G | B⁵ B⁵/F♯ | E⁷ E⁷/B |

Ah ha.

| E⁷ E⁷/B | A G | B⁵ B⁵/F♯ |

| E⁷   E⁷/B ‖

What happened down there?

Verse 4

    E⁷   E⁷/B   A   G
Her husband was a hard working man,
        B⁵   B⁵/F♯   E⁷
Just about a mile and a half from here,
           E⁷/B
What happened to him?
    E⁷   E⁷/B   A   G
His head was found in a driver wheel,
        B⁵   B⁵/F♯   E⁷   E⁷/B
But his body has never been found.

Verse 5

    E⁷   E⁷/B   A   G
My girl, my girl, don't you lie to me.
        B⁵   B⁵/F♯   E⁷
Tell me where did you sleep last night?
           E⁷/B
Come on and tell me something about it.
    E⁷   E⁷/B   A   G
In the pines, in the pines, where the sun don't ever shine,
        B⁵   B⁵/F♯   E⁷   E⁷/B | E⁷ E⁷/B | A   ‖
I would shiver the whole night through.

Who Do You Love?

Words & Music by
Ellas McDaniel

A♭

Intro

E♭ F G
6fr 3fr 5fr
⑤ ④ ④

‖: A♭ G♭ E♭   A♭ :‖ *Play 17 times*
   6fr 4fr 6fr
   ④ ④ ⑥

Verse 1

A♭
    I walk forty-seven miles of barbed wire,

I use a cobra-snake for a necktie,

I got a brand new house on the roadside,

Made from rattlesnake hide,

I got a brand new chimney made on top,

Made out of a human skull,

Now come on take a little walk with me, Arlene,

And tell me, who do you love?

riff 1 ⌐————————————¬
      A♭ B
‖: A♭ 13fr 12fr :‖ *Play 5 times*
    ③ ②

Chorus 1
Who do you love?

Verse 2

A♭
Tombstone hand and a graveyard mine,

Just twenty-two and I don't mind dying.

‖: A♭ w/riff 1 :‖ *Play 4 times*

Chorus 2
Who do you love?

Verse 3

A♭
I rode a - round the town, use a rattlesnake whip,

Take it easy Arlene, don't give me no lip.

Chorus 3

‖: **A♭ w/riff 1**   :‖ *Play 4 times*
Who do you love?

Guitar solo   ‖: **A♭**   :‖ *Play 28 times*

Verse 4

A♭
Night was dark, but the sky was blue,

Down the alley, the ice-wagon flew,

Heard a bump, and somebody screamed,

You should have heard just what I seen.

Chorus 4

‖: **A♭ w/riff 1 *ad lib.*** :‖ *Play 4 times*
Who do you love?

Verse 5

A♭
Arlene took me by my hand,

And she said, "Ow-wee Bo, you know I understand."

Chorus 5

A♭
Who do you love, honey?

Who do you love?

Who do you love?

Who do you love?

Outro   ‖: **A♭**   :‖ *Guitar solo to fade*

Yer Blues

Words & Music by
John Lennon & Paul McCartney

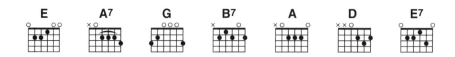

| E | A7 | G | B7 | A | D | E7 |

Verse 1

                  E
Yes, I'm lonely, wanna die,

             A7   **E**
Yes, I'm lonely, wanna die,

             G
If I ain't dead already,

B7   **E A E B7**
Whoo, girl, you know the reason why.

Verse 2

                 E
In the morning, wanna die,

            A7   **E**
In the evening, wanna die,

             G
If I ain't dead already,

B7   **E A E B7**
Whoo, girl, you know the reason why.

Bridge 1

            E N.C.
My mother was of the sky,

D   **E N.C.**
  My father was of the earth,

D   **E N.C.**
  But I am of the universe,

          E7
And you know what it's worth.

Verse 3

         A7   **E**
I'm lonely, wanna die,

             G
If I ain't dead already,

B7   **E A E B7**
Whoo, girl, you know the reason why.

Bridge 2

   E N.C.
The eagle picks my eyes,

  D   E N.C.
  The worm, he licks my bones,

  D E N.C.
  Feel so suicidal,

      E7
Just like Dylan's Mr. Jones.

Verse 4

  A7   E
  Lonely, wanna die,

     G
If I ain't dead already,

B7   E A E B7
Whoo, girl, you know the reason why.

Verse 5

  E   N.C.
Black cloud crossed my mind,

  D E N.C.
  Blue mist from my soul,

  D E N.C.
  Feel so suicidal,

    E7
Even hate my rock and roll.

    A7   E
Wanna die, yeah, wanna die,

     G
If I ain't dead already,

B7   E A E B7
Whoo, girl, you know the reason why.

Solo

| E | E | E | E | A7 | A7 |

| E | E | G | B7 | E A | E B7 ‖

| E | E | E | E | A7 | A7 |

| E | E | G | B7 | E | ‖

Verse 6

    E
(Yes, I'm lonely, wanna die,

    A7   E
Yes, I'm lonely, wanna die,

    G
If I ain't dead already,

B7   E A E B7
Girl, you know the reason why.)   *Fade out*

You Can't Lose What You Ain't Never Had

Words & Music by
Muddy Waters

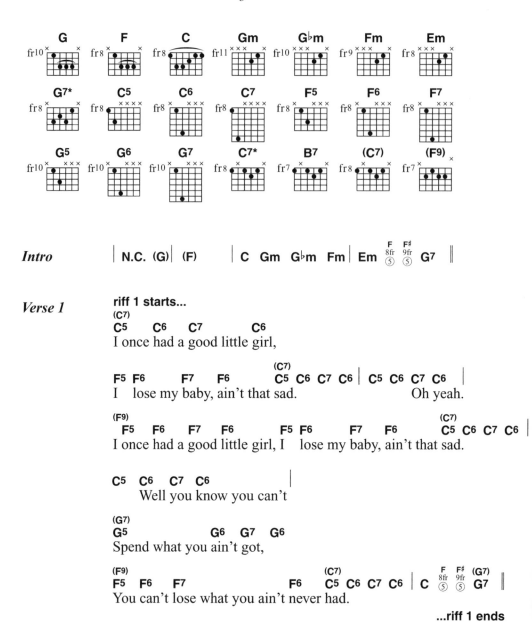

Verse 2

(C7) w/riff 1   **(F9)**   **(C7)**
I had money in the bank, I got busted, boys ain't that sad.

           (F9)
Oh you know, I had some money in the bank,

           (C7)
I got busted, baby ain't that bad.

           (G7)
Well you know you can't spend what you ain't got,

(F9)   C7 | C G7 ‖
You can't lose what you ain't never had.

Instr.

(C7)			
C5 C6 C7 C6	C5 C6 C7 C6	C5 C6 C7 C6	C5 C6 C7 C6
(F9)		**(C7)**	
F5 F6 F7 F6	F5 F6 F7 F6	C5 C6 C7 C6	C5 C6 C7 C6
(G7)	**(F9)**	**(C7)**	**(C7)**
G5 G6 G7 G6	F5 F6 F7 F6	C5 C6 C7 C6	C5 C6 C7 C6 ‖

Verse 3

(C7) w/riff 1   **(F9)**   **(C7)**
I had a sweet little home, it got burned down, boys ain't that bad.

           (F9)   **(C7)**
Oh you know it wasn't my own fault, people ain't that sad.

           (G7)
Well you know you can't spend what you ain't got,

(F9)   **(C7)** | C7 | C G7 ‖ C7 ‖
You can't lose what you ain't never had.

Your Touch

Words & Music by
Daniel Auerbach & Patrick Carney

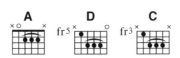

Intro | N.C. (A) | N.C. (D)   N.C. (C) | N.C. (A) | N.C. (D)   N.C. (C) ‖

‖: A | D C | A | D C :‖

Verse 1
A   D C A   D C A
  And I want,   and you got it.
       D C   A   D C
So much,   I'm crazy for it.

Chorus 1
(C)   A   D C   A   D C
Your touch,   your touch.
      A   D C   A   D C
Your touch,   your touch.

Verse 2
A   D C A   D C A
  Yeah and I'd be good   like I should.
        D C A   D C
Waiting inside   misery I need...

Chorus 2   As Chorus 1

Interlude   ‖: A | D C | A | D C :‖

| N.C. (A) | N.C. (D)   N.C. (C) | N.C. (A) | N.C. (D)   N.C. (C) ‖

| A | D C | A | D C ‖

```
                   A          D C     A                    D C A
Verse 3            Ooh Lordy lord…      I got excited now,
                              D C  A           D
                   Please rush,          I need..


                   C    A     D  C     A     D C
Chorus 3           Your touch,       your touch.
                        A     D  C     A     D C A
                   Your touch,       your touch.
```

You Shook Me

Words & Music by
Willie Dixon & J.B. Lenoir

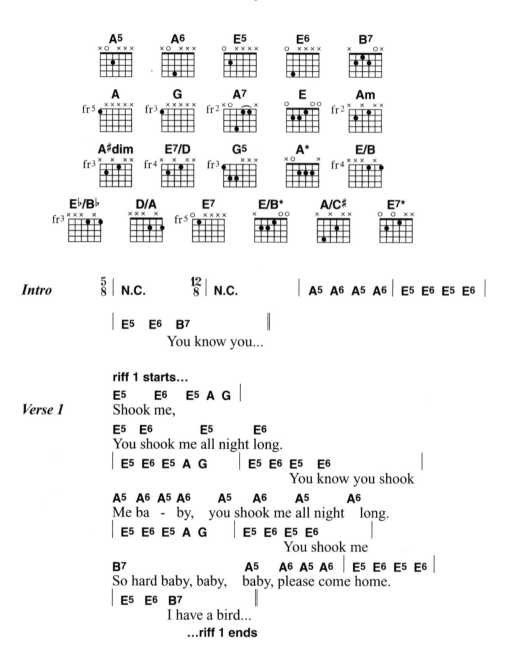

Intro $\frac{5}{8}$ | N.C. $\frac{12}{8}$ | N.C. | A5 A6 A5 A6 | E5 E6 E5 E6 |

| E5   E6   B7   ‖

You know you...

riff 1 starts…

E5   E6   E5 A G |

Verse 1   Shook me,

E5   E6   E5   E6

You shook me all night long.

| E5 E6 E5 A G | E5 E6 E5   E6 |

You know you shook

A5 A6 A5 A6   A5   A6   A5   A6

Me ba - by,   you shook me all night   long.

| E5 E6 E5 A G | E5 E6 E5 E6 |

You shook me

B7   A5   A6 A5 A6 | E5 E6 E5 E6 |

So hard baby, baby,   baby, please come home.

| E5   E6   B7   ‖

I have a bird...

…riff 1 ends

Verse 2

w/riff 1

…That whistles, and I have birds that sing.

I have a bird that whistles, and I have birds that sing.

I have a bird won't do nothing, oh, oh, oh, oh,

Without a diamond ring.

Instr. 1
Organ

| E5   A G | E5 E6 E5 A G | E5 E6 E5 A G |

| E5 E6 E5 A G | A5 A6 A5   G5 | A5 A6 A5   G5 |

| E5 E6 E5 A G | E5 E6 E5 | B7 |

| A7 | E Am A#dim | E7/D   B7 ‖

Instr. 2
Harmonica

| E5 E6 E5 A G | E5 E6 E5 A G | E5 E6 E5 A G |

| A5 E5 E6 E5 | A5   G5 | A* A7 A G5 |

| E5 E6 E5 A G | E5 E6 E5 | B7 |

| A7 | E E/B E♭/B♭ D/A | E   B7 ‖

Instr. 3
Guitar

| E5 E6 E7 E5 E7 E6 | E5 E7/D Am E5 A G |

| E/B* A/C# E/B* A G | E7* E5 |

| A5 N.C. | A5 N.C. | E5 E6 E5 | E6   E5 |

| B7 | A7 | E Am A#dim | E7/D (B7)N.C. ‖

You know you...

Verse 3

E5   **E6**   **E5**   **A G** |
Shook   me babe,

E5   **E6**   **E5**   **E6** | **E5 E6 E5 A G** |
You shook me all   night long.

| **E5 E6 E5 E6** |
   I know you really, really did babe. I think you

A5   **A6**   **A5**
Shook   me, baby.

   A5 **A6**   **A5**   **A6** | **E5 E6 E5 A G** |
You   shook me all night   long,

| **E5 E6 E5 E6** |
   You shook me

B7   **A7**   **N.C.** *freetime*
So hard, baby, babe, I know,

| Oh ah, oh, oh | oh, oh, oh | oh, no, no | oh, no, no |

You shook me | all | all night | long. |

| **A5** **E** ‖